The Transformation of the Western Region

Author Royalties from this book are being donated to Mental Health Charity Mates in Mind
https://matesinmind.org

To Gary
You are absolutely part of this
Best wishes Paul Stanford

Paul Stanford

SLP
A Silver Link Limited Edition
Published 6 December 2018

The Transformation of the Western Region

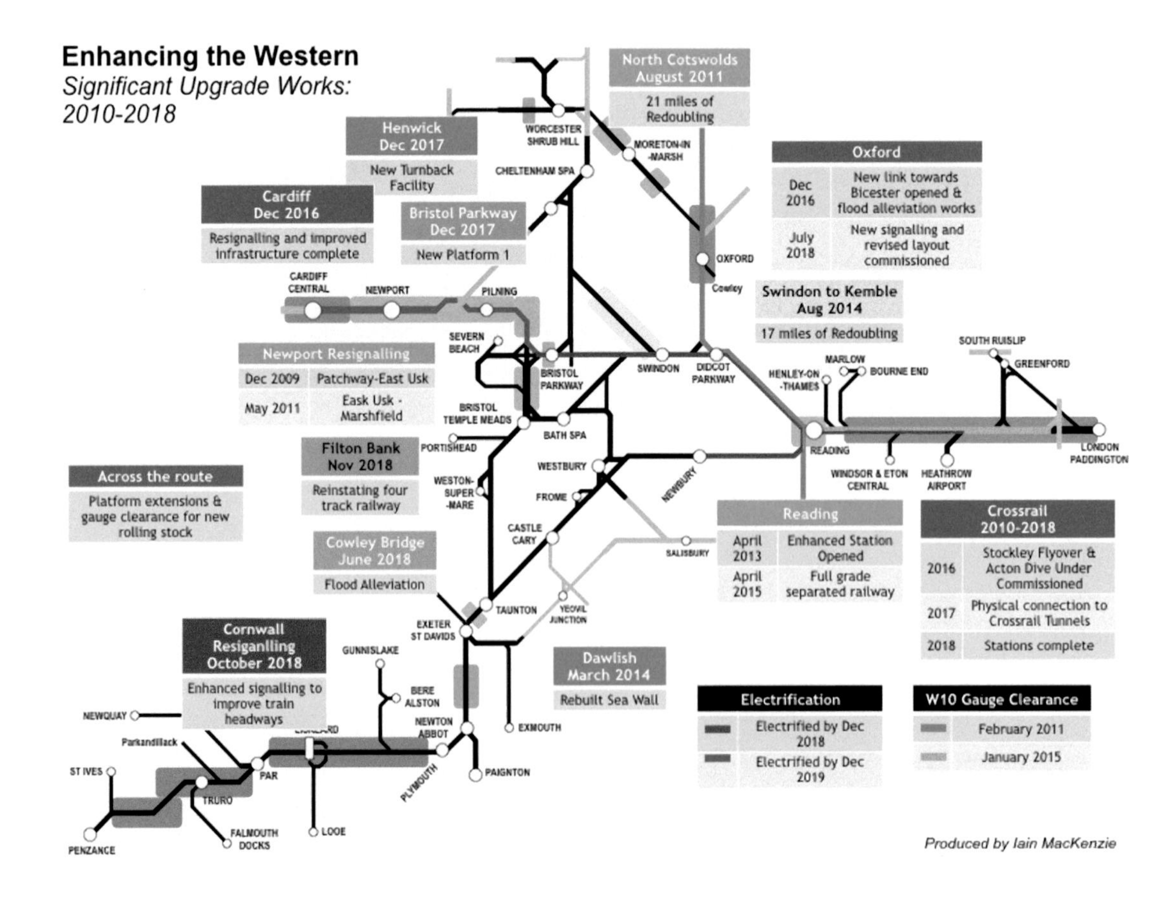

Enhancing the Western
Significant Upgrade Works: 2010-2018
North Cotswolds August 2011
21 miles of Redoubling
Henwick Dec 2017
New Turnback Facility
Cardiff Dec 2016
Resignalling and improved infrastructure complete
Bristol Parkway Dec 2017
New Platform 1
Oxford
Dec 2016
New link towards Bicester opened & flood alleviation works
July 2018
New signalling and revised layout commissioned
Swindon to Kemble Aug 2014
17 miles of Redoubling
Newport Resignalling
Dec 2009
Patchway-East Usk
May 2011
Eask Usk - Marshfield
Filton Bank Nov 2018
Reinstating four track railway
Across the route
Platform extensions & gauge clearance for new rolling stock
Cowley Bridge June 2018
Flood Alleviation
Reading
April 2013
Enhanced Station Opened
April 2015
Full grade separated railway
Crossrail 2010-2018
2016
Stockley Flyover & Acton Dive Under Commissioned
2017
Physical connection to Crossrail Tunnels
2018
Stations complete
Cornwall Resiganlling October 2018
Enhanced signalling to improve train headways
Dawlish March 2014
Rebuilt Sea Wall
Electrification
Electrified by Dec 2018
Electrified by Dec 2019
W10 Gauge Clearance
February 2011
January 2015
WORCESTER SHRUB HILL
MORETON-IN-MARSH
CHELTENHAM SPA
OXFORD
Cowley
CARDIFF CENTRAL
NEWPORT
PILNING
SEVERN BEACH
BRISTOL PARKWAY
SWINDON
DIDCOT PARKWAY
SOUTH RUISLIP
GREENFORD
MARLOW
BOURNE END
HENLEY-ON-THAMES
BRISTOL TEMPLE MEADS
BATH SPA
READING
LONDON PADDINGTON
PORTISHEAD
WESTBURY
WINDSOR & ETON CENTRAL
HEATHROW AIRPORT
WESTON-SUPER-MARE
FROME
NEWBURY
CASTLE CARY
SALISBURY
TAUNTON
YEOVIL JUNCTION
EXETER ST DAVIDS
GUNNISLAKE
BERE ALSTON
NEWQUAY
NEWTON ABBOT
EXMOUTH
Parkandillack
PAR
PLYMOUTH
PAIGNTON
ST IVES
TRURO
FALMOUTH DOCKS
LOOE
PENZANCE
Produced by Iain MacKenzie

The Transformation of the Western Region
2010-2018

Paul Stanford

Foreword by Pete Waterman OBE

Silver Link Publishing Ltd

First published in 2018

ISBN 978 1 85794 543 0 (Limited Edition)
978 1 85794 544 7 (Standard Edition)

British Library Cataloguing in Publication Data
A catalogue record for this book is available from the British Library.

Silver Link Publishing Ltd
The Trundle
Ringstead Road
Great Addington
Kettering
Northants NN14 4BW

Tel/Fax: 01536 330588
email: sales@nostalgiacollection.com
Website: www.nostalgiacollection.com

Printed and bound in the Czech Republic

Acknowledgements

This book would not have been possible if Network Rail had not been involved with leading the renewal and upgrade works that have transformed the Western Region, primarily funded by the Department for Transport, and which created the photographic opportunities. So I thank my colleagues who had the foresight to capture the works as they happened, sometimes in snow or rain, often during anti-social hours, and sometimes only with a camera phone, so please forgive the photographic quality at times.

I am extremely grateful to my friend Iain Mackenzie for his excellent maps reflecting works across the region, together with Martin Duff for his signalling plans and photographs.

My very special thanks go to Richard Griffiths, Rob Mashford, Richard Scott, Tom Woodworth, Peter Hall, Matthew Thompson and Emily Papworth who went to special lengths to get me photographs or indeed took them for me. My late father John Stanford contributed through the use of his archive photos from the 1960s and '70s.

A special word of thanks is due to Mark Hopwood, GWR Managing Director, who kindly consented to waiving commercial photography charges at stations and his wider support

I am extremely grateful to Neil Thompson for his support and help with the production of this book, and the same needs to be said of Kathryn Stephens, Pete Waterman, Sir Peter Hendy and Mark Langman for their enthusiasm and contribution, which spurred me to completion.

A penultimate acknowledgment is to my peers in the wider railway family, to which I've belonged for more than 34 years, embodying Network Rail, the train operators and the supply chain. The scale of the works from 2010 onwards pushed railway people to the very limit, whether it was work complexity, financing, the volume of line possessions, terrible weather conditions for work, managing signal boxes, or maintenance with reduced capability as the works happened, through to facing the need to divert trains or to face irate customers who were weary of getting onto a bus. So a special thank you.

Finally, two very special words of thanks: to my wife Fiona for helping with the production of the book, and my late father John Stanford who inspired me at the age of 15, when he produced his first transport publication, that one day I might do the same.

Contents

Acknowledgements	4
Foreword by Pete Waterman OBE	6
Preface by Network Rail Chairman Sir Peter Hendy CBE	7
Introduction	7
1 Paddington to Maidenhead	9
2 Reading and Didcot	50
3 Swindon	72
4 Wootton Bassett Junction to Bath Spa	81
5 Bristol Temple Meads to Penzance	87
6 Swindon (Wootton Bassett Junction) to Cardiff	109

Foreword by Pete Waterman OBE

When I took my first railway journey the Great Western had only just become the Western Region of British Railways. It was from Leamington Spa to Weston-super-Mare and although too young to remember I must have got the bug, as I spent most of my life following and loving everything Great Western.

Paul's book shows what it takes to rebuild a railway, not only the task itself but the work and planning it takes. In some ways Brunel had the easy job. When he built the route from Paddington to Bristol he didn't have a railway that had to keep running or meet all of today's health and safety standards. The only thing that Network Rail and Brunel had in common was that its army of workers were out in all sorts of weather.

The job of modernising our railway is massive; despite modern equipment it's a long and expensive undertaking.

The book shows only too well the size of the job. In the last ten years we have seen a massive change in railway infrastructure. At last we have woken up to the fact that railways always were the way to travel. Such undertakings are not cheap, not easy and sometimes unpopular with some of the public. Railways are not the answer to all the transport problems but, as part of an integrated transport vision, worth their weight in gold.

Pete Waterman OBE

Preface by Network Rail Chairman Sir Peter Hendy CBE

I have lived on the Great Western Main Line since I was born, at Hayes, in Ealing and latterly for 26 years in Bath, and have seen how much it has changed over the time I have been using it. In my youth, no one could have commuted from Bath to London – now hundreds do. As a boy my train to the dentist at Paddington was hauled by a '61xx' Class tank engine with compartment coaches, and main-line trains were hauled by 'Castles' and 'Kings'. What a change from today and tomorrow!

In my working career I have been part of the development and building of the Elizabeth Line (Crossrail), which when it opens will further transform the Great Western. The whole Great Western transformation will provide greater connectivity to, from and within the West of England, allowing London's wealth to spread wider and foster economic growth, leading to more jobs and houses.

Introduction

The Western Region is a key part of the UK rail network, stretching from London to Penzance, to Worcester via Oxford, and through to South Wales via Bristol. It embodies some challenging railway along the way: from coastal stretches, steep gradients and one of the longest UK rail tunnels to traversing some of the biggest towns and cities, one of which is a World Heritage Site in the form of Bath.

The region witnesses many different train categories every day, ranging from long-distance inter-city trains, local branch passenger trains, commuter trains, inter-regional trains, sleeping car trains and long-distance freight trains, ranging from those conveying containerised product to some of Britain's heaviest freight trains from the Somerset quarries through to china clay trains, which never leave Cornwall.

Unlike the East and West Coast Main Lines, the Western Region has until now not seen the transformational changes that those routes have experienced in the last 50 years, missing out on electrification and grade-separated junctions, with the exception of Heathrow Airport Junction. Instead the Western had seen incremental resignalling schemes and the retention of diesel traction as its primary form of traction during those 50 years.

The Western Region enacted a work stream of eradicating mechanical signal boxes from the 1960s, with a stop-go approach dependent on funding. Bristol Temple Meads, Reading and Oxford, however, had not seen large-scale remodelling schemes for many years, and several lifetimes ago. The 1980s were a low point when, after the Beaching cuts of the 1960s, Western lines were singled or de-quadrupled as rail was no longer fashionable; almost lost in the 1980s was the Bath to Westbury line, which was going to be singled with a passing loop at Trowbridge; happily, it is now a busy double-tracked mixed-traffic route.

Happily, by the mid-1990s the Western Region was experiencing freight and passenger growth that started to reach such levels that simple timetable changes could not accommodate growth or with which the current rolling stock could cope.

The Reading remodelling scheme started in earnest in 2010, and shortly afterwards the on-network Crossrail works (both east and west of London on Network Rail lines) also started, then in the summer of 2009 came the announcement from the Government that the core Western Region was to be electrified. These facets combined, with other works, to bring about the biggest change to the region's railway for many generations.

Work did not always go smoothly, and electrification was paused in 2015 on cost and programme grounds and reviewed by Sir Peter Hendy; after the review some works were not pursued. The large majority did, however, progress and have changed the face of the railway, giving greater train capacity, more and longer trains, refurbished or new stations, and multiple new train fleets controlled by new signalling equipment with a new style of overhead line system.

This book does not seek to capture every event since 2010, but instead hopes to give a flavour of the work's complexity, scale and execution, and its benefits to the region's rail users, publicly sharing photographs not normally seen by the travelling public and students of rail operations. In this area some grace is sought: sometimes photographs weren't of professional quality as people saw something historic during an engineering possession and snapped it with a camera phone.

The book also seeks to reflect in some cases the scale of change, with some 'before and after' photographs. It also seeks to capture the social element, with some photographs showing people as they went about the business of running or transforming the railway. Not to be overlooked are the works on the North and South Cotswold lines, although there is very little coverage in this book as they were adequately covered in other recommended Silver Link books.

For the purposes of the book, the historic term Western Region is used to describe the railway from Paddington to Penzance, Cardiff and Worcester and all points in between.

1. PADDINGTON to MAIDENHEAD

This predominately four-track section of railway through Slough was signalled by three signal boxes, two at Slough itself and Reading Panel Signal Box. British Rail initiated an electrification scheme for 'Heathrow Express' from Paddington to a new junction at milepost 12, where a new branch to Heathrow was constructed and opened in 1997/98.

The new upgrade works initially focused on the Reading area, with a large blockade over Christmas 2010 when Reading signal box was decommissioned; subsequently the two signal boxes at Slough were closed by Easter 2015, and all three locations saw signalling recontrolled and enhanced.

The works necessary for Crossrail trains extended from Paddington to Maidenhead and saw

Network Rail funded by Crossrail to undertake capacity enhancement works. In summary, these works amounted to £1.4 billion and consisted of:

- A reconfigured layout on the Paddington approaches to allow for the new double junction into the Crossrail Central Tunnel Section
- A reconfigured and enhanced track and signal layout around Old Oak Common,

PADDINGTON On 27 December 2017 the station is bereft of trains as Platforms 1 and 2 are electrified ready for the May timetable when new inter-city electric trains will start using the platforms. Given the location of these works, Christmas was the only time for their execution. On this day GWR passenger trains operated into London Marylebone, repeating something done in 2016.

where the Crossrail traincare depot was located

- A new yard junction layout at Acton and, the most substantial feature, a new diveunder
- A new layout at West Ealing, with a new junction to and from the Greenford line, allied to the installation of a bay platform and bay line. Beyond West Ealing a new ladder junction was installed at Southall, and at Hayes an new facing crossover.
- Huge civil, track and signalling works beyond Hayes to double the capacity of the flyover at Stockley Junction
- A new crossover and reconfigured fifth line at West Drayton, including new signalling to and from the Colnbrook freight branch
- A new layout at the west end of Slough station
- A new layout east and west of Maidenhead station, with new stabling sidings at the west end for Crossrail trains

Works have also been carried out at most stations to lengthen platforms and in some cases provide new station buildings.

Additionally non-Crossrail works have taken place on this route section, including a new junction to North Pole depot for the new inter-city trains, extended platforms and additional electrification of the low- and high-numbered platforms at Paddington, the construction and electrification of EMU stabling sidings at West Ealing, electrification of Royal Oak stabling sidings, and resignalling schemes for the two Slough signal boxes, as well as major works to renew trackwork as part of the normal renewals programme.

PADDINGTON On 16 September 2016, a few days after the new GWR Paddington to Hayes electric train service started, one of the new-build trains stands under the refurbished roof at Paddington, with a GWR Class 165 unit on the left-hand side.

PADDINGTON In April 1974 the prototype HST stands at Paddington, having completed a test run from Bristol Temple Meads, on which the author's father, John Stanford, had travelled as part of a contingent of BR staff invited to give their views from the passenger perspective. Forty years later the same happened with the new IEP (Inter-city Express Project) trains. Of note are the lorries on the platform for mail and parcel traffic. Mail traffic at Paddington ceased in 1996 with the new rail depot opening at Wembley.

PADDINGTON Late at night in May 2018 a new Crossrail train is viewed from the first-floor offices overlooking Platform 1, Queen Victoria's viewpoint when she was waiting to board a train to Windsor.

PADDINGTON This was the view in May 2015 looking from the first-floor offices on platform 1 to the street. The works in view are not Network Rail but executed by Crossrail Ltd; however, they involved Network Rail with changes to the usage of the station. The two companies worked closely together for the life of the Crossrail works. Beneath the works here is the new Paddington low-level station.

PADDINGTON On 27 December 2015 platform extension works are under way for the new trains. The picture, looking towards Old Oak Common, shows the cramped nature of the site where the work was being undertaken. Aside from the platform extension this and the adjacent line were electrified.

PADDINGTON On the same date, the view of the other side of the island platform shows the repositioned platform coping stones to cater for the new-build trains. Of note are the lines that were relayed the previous Christmas, for both Network Rail and London Underground, with both bodies helping one another with their respective track works.

PADDINGTON At the Didcot Thames Valley Signalling Centre, this is a signaller's view of the works in Platforms 14 and 13, the track circuit indications showing red (occupied), which in this case indicates the presence of road-rail vehicles. While this and other works on the Paddington-Acton corridor were taking place over Christmas 2015 GWR trains ran in and out of Paddington with Network Rail financing pilot drivers from Freightliner to pilot High Speed Trains over the Chiltern route, a far more practical and pleasant proposition than bussing people.

Above: **PADDINGTON** In November 2014 *Pendennis Castle* – the diesel version – stands at the buffer stops, having bought in the empty coaching stock for the Penzance sleeper train. Above the locomotive is the decking that was progressively repositioned under the canopy as the restoration work occurred during a two-year programme – challenging work that could be disrupted by an unplanned train left in the station, affecting short night-time possession windows.

Right: **PADDINGTON** On 10 October 2017 Network Rail Delivery Director Graeme Tandy stands next to inspection saloon *Caroline* before its 10.00 departure to Swindon. Graeme led the work to electrify the railway from Maidenhead to Bristol Parkway and Newbury.

PADDINGTON Locomotive No 37425 is about to set off on the scheduled inspection special train to Swindon propelling the inspection saloon *Caroline*. These inspection trains are operated to allow asset and project managers to view the state of the infrastructure.

PADDINGTON A 'Heathrow Express' unit runs into the station, viewed from Enterprise House, the home for some of the Network Rail project staff working on the Crossrail programme. Where the tower blocks stand behind the train was formerly Paddington Goods Depot. The photo emphasises the cramped nature of present-day Paddington, making it a challenge to undertake the track relaying in 2015 and reconfigure of overhead wiring in the period 2014-18 for Crossrail trains and the new inter-city trains.

Above: **PADDINGTON** GWR's No 57606 looks superb standing at the buffer stops on the sleeper train from Penzance, with the refurbished roof shown to good advantage at 06.18 on the morning of 10 August 2016 – photographed as the author returned from a family holiday via Heathrow.

Left: **PADDINGTON** In this scene on 17 April 2010 an ex-GWR 'Castle' Class locomotive No 5043 *Earl of Mount Edgecumbe* is about to haul a Paddington-Bristol-Paddington charter. After this special run a conscious reduction in charter trains occurred because of the upgrade works, which meant reduced capacity through Reading. The return run of this train was notable for arriving Paddington 45 minutes early – the author was the nominated Network Rail representative on the train and he liaised in real time with Swindon control – every signal was green from Bristol to the Paddington station approaches.

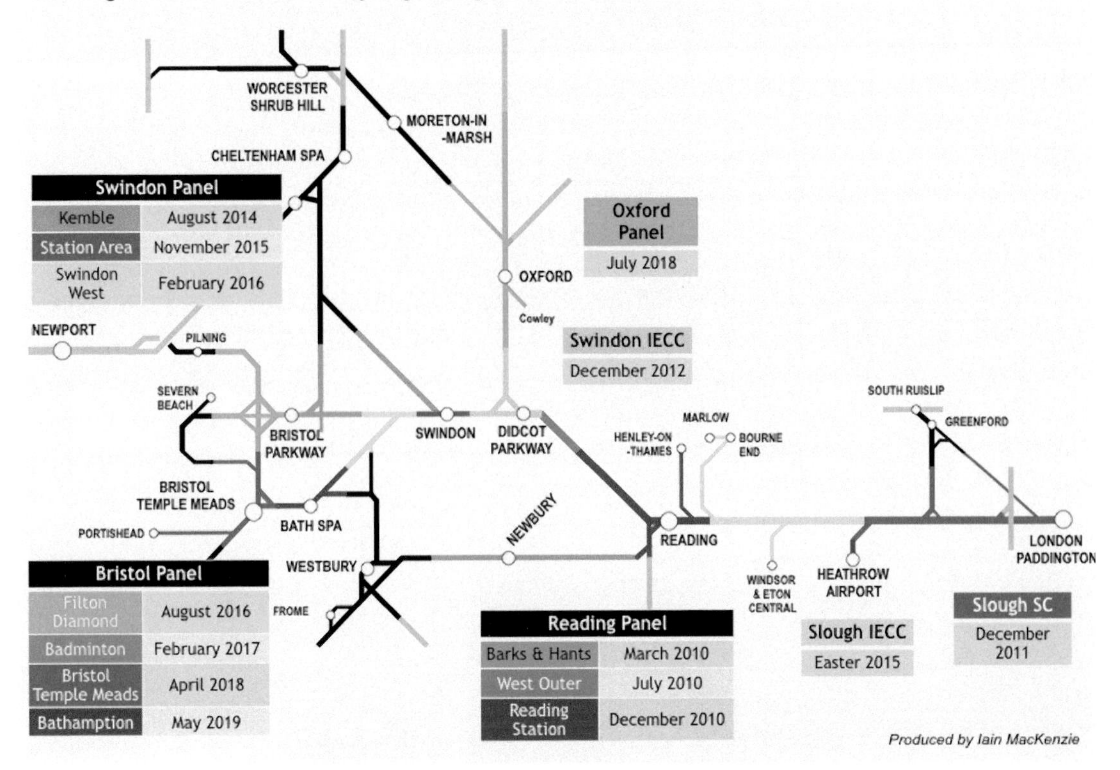

PADDINGTON workstation is seen again on the Didcot Integrated Electronic Control Centre (IECC) on 28 December 2015. 2010 saw the first IECC signalling control instituted for the Reading area, followed by Slough (both signal boxes), then Swindon (both signal boxes), and from 2016 the progressive closure of signal control positions at Bristol.

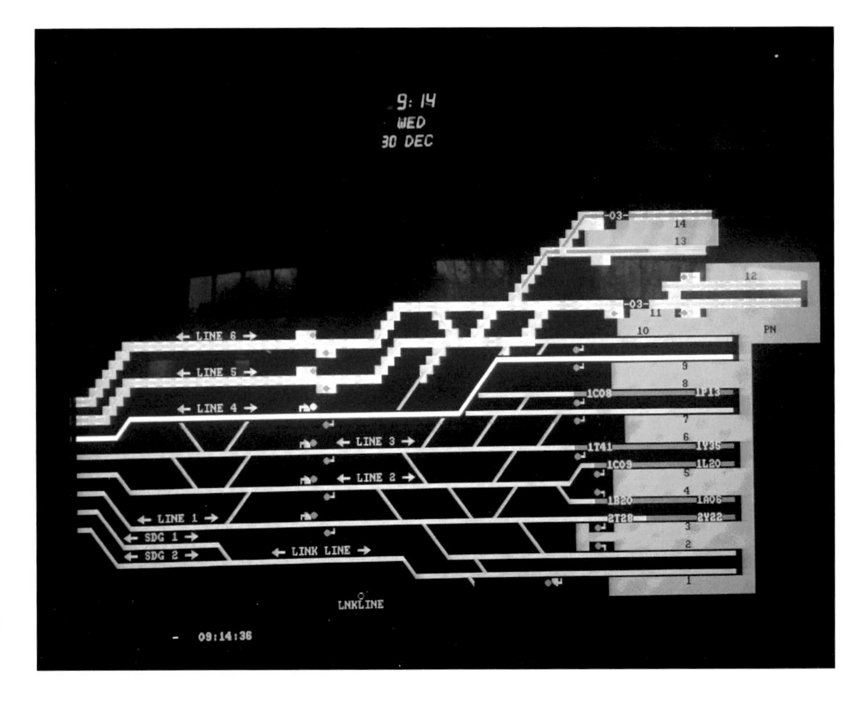

PADDINGTON On 27 December 2015 track relaying is taking place in Platform 13 on a new alignment, and station platform coping stones are being installed. During this Network Rail work the adjacent Hammersmith & City Line was also relayed in a joint operation, believed to be a first. London Underground locomotive No 23 and Colas Rail No 70810 are seen hauling their respective logistics trains.

Left: **PADDINGTON** On the evening of 15 August 2018 this view, soon to change, captures two HSTs and their modern replacement. Platforms 1 and 2 were overhead wired during Christmas 2017.

PADDINGTON During that same night the rolling stock for the Paddington to Penzance sleeper is seen in the electrified Platform 1. Some two years after the station roof was restored, the beauty of the spans is still evident.

PADDINGTON On 16 August 2018 a Paddington to Bristol GWR IEP train departs from Platform 1, alongside the area formerly used in the late 1990s and early 2000s for the Motorail service. In this constrained area the far side of the layout is where additional electrification took place, unknown to most travellers, to give GWR and Crossrail electric trains access to the high-numbered platforms.

PADDINGTON On the same day a Crossrail train draws into the platform that was lengthened during the works executed over 2015-16. Aside from platform works, gauging also took place to allow these smart new trains to operate between Paddington to Heathrow.

Left and opposite page: **PADDINGTON** The works of Christmas 2015 and 2016, evident in these photographs taken on 14 August 2018, saw the lengthening and regauging of several platforms and the electrification of the station's high-numbered platforms to enable Crossrail Class 345 EMUs and their GWR counterparts to operate.

THE GAP

MARYLEBONE station's departure screen on 27 December 2017 is a giveaway to the fact that the GW Main Line is closed, with the 14.42 train to Swansea being shown, which ran through Princes Risborough then via the new chord line at Bicester before calling at Oxford and heading round Foxhall Curve at Didcot to pick up the scheduled route to South Wales.

MARYLEBONE On the same day an HST is ready to depart for Swansea, standing alongside a Chiltern Railways Class 168 unit. Diversions such as this are a significant logistic issue for train companies, having to arrange train water-tanking, staff route knowledge and train cleaning.

ROYAL OAK In July 2012 a narrow-gauge train leaves the Crossrail tunnel with a people-carrier vehicle and grouting wagons as a 'Heathrow Connect' train heads into London Paddington. The narrow-gauge (900mm) railway operated for just over two years until 2014 in support of the building of the tunnels by Crossrail Ltd. Network Rail and Crossrail staff worked closely on what is now completed as a new standard-gauge double junction off the GW Main Line and into the central London tunnels, as well as wider collaboration on the works for Crossrail services.

ROYAL OAK Looking in the opposite direction towards Old Oak Common in March 2015, the narrow-gauge lines have gone, to be replaced by standard-gauge sidings that fulfilled a role as a logistics railhead, which was progressively extended into the new-build tunnels. Over the fence Network Rail staff lead work to reposition track and overhead wires over several years to facilitate the new junction that exists by the Westway.

ROYAL OAK On the penultimate day of September 2018 a new Class 345 train stands on the lines leading to the tunnel mouth of the Central Tunnel Section of the Crossrail network.

WESTBOURNE PARK On 30 December 2016, looking towards Paddington, new overhead line equipment (OLE) booms are installed using road-rail plant. Where the sun is rising is dominated by the Westway.

ROYAL OAK Leaving the station heading onto the Great Western Main Line, the adjacent Crossrail works are evident; much changed from the photo showing the narrow-gauge construction train. This picture was taken on 16 August 2018 as Crossrail Ltd undertook the final fit-out – these works were enabled by Network Rail track slews and the attendant changes to the overhead wire system. A Clayton built locomotive is in view to shunt the logistics terminal.

ROYAL OAK Much of the Crossrail works happened after dark on weeknights, as seen here, with large-scale realignment of the OLE taking place to prepare for Crossrail trains and to support the Crossrail works linked to lines into the new tunnels.

WESTBOURNE PARK Looking towards Paddington on May Bank Holiday 2016, the Engine and Carriage lines (which run between Paddington and Old Oak Common) are being relayed as part of the realignment of the track to create the new junction with the Crossrail tunnels.

OLD OAK COMMON Seen on the night of Christmas Day 2014, the Engine and Carriage lines cross over the Great Western Main Line to avoid a flat junction with points and crossings. A full track relay is under way as in the future these lines will be the means by which Crossrail trains will access their new depot at Old Oak.

OLD OAK COMMON On the night of Christmas Day 2015 the track relay is in full swing as a tracked vehicle lifts track sections into place.

OLD OAK COMMON On 27 December 2015 the finishing touches are made to the relaid track on the Engine and Carriage lines. In the distance are Mitre Bridge and Scrubbs Lane Bridge, which were both refurbished in 2017, in advance of the start of Crossrail services. The works on the Engine and Carriage lines also saw them electrified and resignalled in readiness for the start of Crossrail services.

OLD OAK COMMON Looking towards Slough at Easter 2016, a deep dig operation is under way prior to installing part of a new track layout; on the left are 'Coalfish' wagons, used to convey spoil, while on the right are auto-ballaster wagons loaded with fresh ballast.

ACTON The track works at this location happened over several years from 2014 to 2016 in available windows between train services, so this typically meant large set work pieces at Christmas and Easter. This photograph was taken on the night of 28 December 2014. A train of 'Coalfish' wagons stands alongside the work – these wagons are used to carry new ballast to or spoil from track relaying works.

Above: **ACTON** The diveunder is seen in April 2015, with initial sheet piles and spray-creting having taken place. The timetable modelling of 2012/13 for the Thames Valley in connection with the new Crossrail trains indicated the benefits that a diveunder would generate, allowing trains to pass through the area on the Up Relief as a jumbo stone train departs or enters the freight yard.

Right: **ACTON YARD** On the approach to the new diveunder in the spring of 2105, No 66003 stands at the head of a rake of auto-ballasters preparing to drop ballast on the newly laid lines. The auto-ballasters are remotely controlled by one operator, a far cry from legions of people with 'Dogfish' wagons manually operating the ballast wagon doors.

ACTON This is the diveunder above ground on the morning of Boxing Day 2015. The excavation was begun in October 2013 following nearly two years of work to reconfigure the freight yard, which involved moving the tracks in it 8 metres to the north, line by line, over multiple weekends. In this picture, looking towards Paddington, the Kirow crane is positioning trackwork over the diveunder. Work on the diveunder continued as trains ran on either side of the excavation heading to and from Acton Yard.

ACTON On Good Friday 2016 Colas Rail No 70804 passes with a train of track sections as draining works are undertaken. The two lines nearest the camera are the access/egress lines for Acton Yard and are at the point where they pass over the diveunder, which at this time was in its final stages of completion.

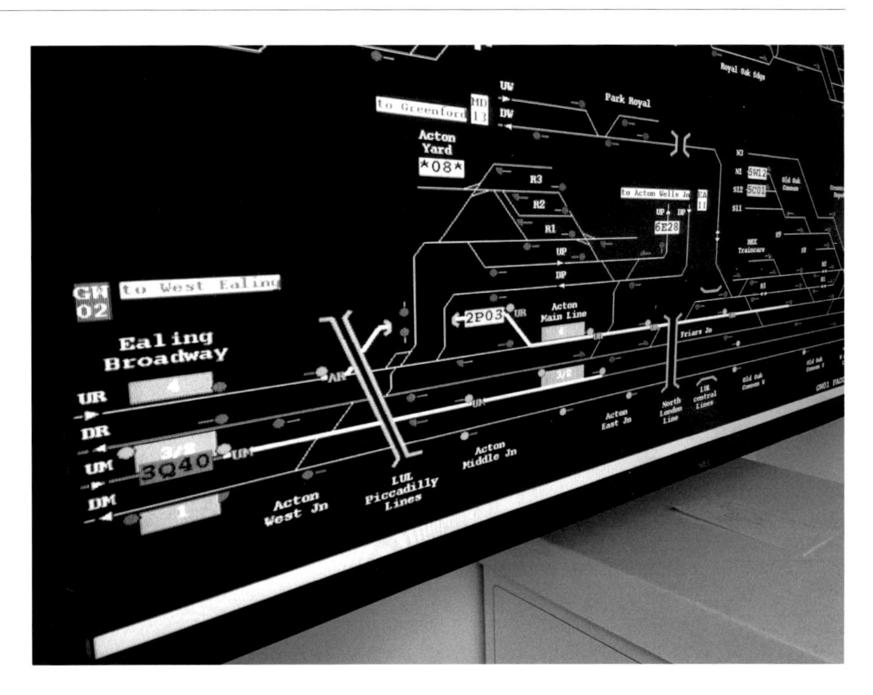

ACTON On 3 January 2017 the diveunder is seen on the overview screen in Swindon Network Rail Control, with the first public train (headcode 2P03, centre of picture) travelling through it – the author was determined to capture the first train to use the new line. The schematic diagram illustrates well the benefits that the new diveunder brings, easing the operation of Acton Freight Yard as well as upholding timely operations on the Relief lines.

EALING BROADWAY On Boxing Day 2015 the new footbridge is installed, linked to readiness for future Crossrail operations.

EALING BROADWAY On the same day this was the moment at when the new bridge was lifted during a period when no trains were operating. The bridge came into its own during the Christmas 2016 blockade in this area, with passenger trains terminating here.

EALING BROADWAY After a successful lift-in of the bridge, it's smiles all round by relieved staff. Christmas periods proved the ideal time to undertake Network Rail works for the Crossrail programme, with no or limited impact on train services. The rust on the fast lines on the left affirms that all lines are closed.

EALING BROADWAY Christmas Eve 2016 saw the start of a major six-day operation with the lines blocked east of Ealing Broadway to allow large-scale track and signal works through Acton, Old Oak Common and around Paddington. This called for an army of volunteers on the four days that passenger trains ran, as they started and terminated at Ealing Broadway instead of Paddington. In this photograph Barry Milsom (left) and Richard Rowland of GWR take a break from Customer Assist duties. The passenger operation won Network Rail and GWR an award from the Chartered Institute of Transport & Logistics for 'Passenger Transport Best Practice' in 2017.

EALING BROADWAY On the morning of Christmas Eve 2016 a Bristol Temple Meads train terminates at the station with lines ahead blocked beyond the station crossover points while Crossrail works took place between Acton Yard and London Paddington. The author travelled on this train and spent the day with Network Rail and GWR colleagues volunteering to help passengers transferring between main-line services and the Central Line.

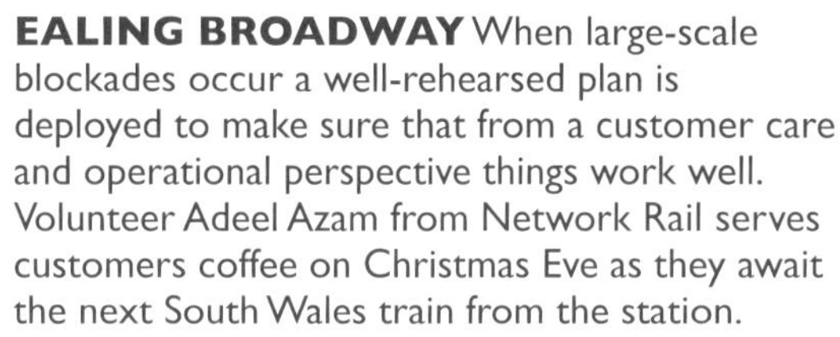

EALING BROADWAY When large-scale blockades occur a well-rehearsed plan is deployed to make sure that from a customer care and operational perspective things work well. Volunteer Adeel Azam from Network Rail serves customers coffee on Christmas Eve as they await the next South Wales train from the station.

EALING BROADWAY One of the new 'banner repeater' signals, commissioned with the Slough resignalling works of 2014/15, is evident on Christmas Eve 2016 as an Ealing Broadway to Bristol train starts its journey.

WEST EALING Looking towards Greenford on 5 January 2016, DB Cargo No 66067 passes slowly over newly installed plain line and pointwork. The junction was reconfigured to a single-lead junction, to create the track configuration for a new bay platform.

WEST EALING On 30 December 2015, with the Plasser Works just out of sight to the left, a train of wagons is conveying recovered sleepers, which will be recycled. Running from left to right in the distance is the other part of the line forming a triangle at this location.

WEST EALING Looking towards London Paddington on 1 January 2016, the newly installed bay platform can be seen on the left, together with the reconfigured overhead lines. As part of this work a specific timetable modelling exercise took place, with the reduction of the track from a double junction to a single lead. The reconfigured junction allowed a platform extension for new trains.

SOUTHALL At Christmas 2015 the Kirow crane is lifting new plain line trackwork into place opposite the old Southall Depot, now used by Locomotive Services Limited. A further part of the old Southall Depot Yard is used by the Great Western Preservation Group, owner of several ex-GWR steam locomotives.

SOUTHALL Looking in the opposite direction, Volker Rail's Kirow crane works between the steam depot and Southall station. This view is looking towards Bristol (and Southall station). Of note is the challenge for the crane operator to work under the overhead wires. The telescopic jibs on these type of crane make this work easier.

SOUTHALL Looking towards Paddington on New Year's Day 2016, platform extension works are taking place to cater for the new nine-car Crossrail trains. Just catching the light is Merrick Road Footbridge, and beyond the floodlights indicate the Southall steam shed used by Locomotive Services Limited.

HAYES & HARLINGTON On 1 May 2016, looking towards Slough, the Down and Up Relief lines are closed and the platform extension works are under way to accommodate the new Crossrail trains. Also noticeable in this shot are the Driver Operation TV screens needed by the new Crossrail services.

HAYES & HARLINGTON On 3 January 2017 at the London end of the station staff are working on the platform extension, ready for the new Crossrail Class 345 trains; it will also prove an early benefit for GWR's Class 387 EMUs. The road-railer stands on the Down Relief line, as an scheduled HST passes on the Up Main line to London Paddington. This shot epitomises the period 2014 to 2018 during the Crossrail West works, with weekends regularly seeing a two-track timetable and the other two lines blocked for the upgrade works.

HAYES & HARLINGTON On Easter Saturday 2016, looking towards London, staff relay the Relief lines, linked to the installation of the new layout. The Fast lines are on the left.

HAYES Roger Webster beautifully captured the scene at Hayes in July 1963, when things looked tranquil, very different from today. The view is towards Reading. On the right a rake of parcel vans sits in the bay platform now used by electric trains operated either by GWR or TfL Crossrail. Thirty years after Roger's picture in 1993 agreement was reached to build the Heathrow rail link.

STOCKLEY FLYOVER This view from 26 December 2015, looking towards Heathrow Airport and Reading, gives an indication of the scale of what was installed here from 2012. The new bridge and associated ramp are visible on the right, coming into use in 2016. Of note are the staff wearing communications equipment, used between the road-rail machine operators and staff on the ground controlling movements.

Above: **STOCKLEY FLYOVER** Also looking towards Heathrow and Reading on the previous day, staff take a break from the installation of new signalling equipment following the laying of the new track. Beyond them is the new bridge; which doubles the capacity of the flyover lines, supporting the new Crossrail train services. The bridge is named 'Sams Bridge' after Richard Sams, who had been the project engineer on the Stockley project from its inception in 2011 and whose work on the project played a major part in ensuring its success. Richard died suddenly in 2014 while on holiday in Mexico, so the bridge is a fitting tribute to him.

Left: **STOCKLEY FLYOVER** Now looking towards Paddington on 28 December 2015, this photograph was taken from Sams Bridge. The view shows concrete 'kerb' sections being craned into place as part of the finishing works, which enhanced the capability of the flyover to deal with more trains.

STOCKLEY FLYOVER Looking towards Reading in December 2015, this night view shows the central section of the new flyover being constructed with a Kirow crane lifting in sections as a road-railer rests from its work.

WEST DRAYTON Looking toward Hayes & Harlington, one of the largest rail-road vehicles in the UK, with a telescopic jib, runs between worksites on 28 December 2015. It is travelling on the Down Relief line supporting electrification work and the erection of masts.

SLOUGH Aside from Network Rail's Construction Managers, the other people key to the real-time railway and its upgrade works are the Mobile Operations Managers. Here MOMs Jane and Alan share a joke on Royal Wedding Day 2018 at Slough with two British Transport Police Community Support Officers. MOMs, like Construction Managers, can fix issues in real time, as well as check on the quality of works, undertake inspections within their discipline, and be the first point of contact for going to a site where an issue exists, through to the less positive aspects such as attendance at a fatality.

TAPLOW On 26 December 2015, looking towards Paddington, staff engaged by Balfour Beatty are installing OLE. The former goods yard was on the right.

MAIDENHEAD Looking towards Paddington at Christmas 2015 a road-railer is engaged in sheet piling the embankment to allow for a new layout at the east end of the station for when Crossrail services commence.

MAIDENHEAD Track relaying on the Relief lines is in full swing in this view looking towards Paddington in March 2016. The road-railer machines are invaluable for the positioning of concrete sleepers, and with a special fitment can thread single rails onto newly laid sleepers.

MAIDENHEAD On Boxing Day 2015 Tarek Chamseddine talks to the (then) Network Rail Chief Executive through the Christmas 2015 works at Maidenhead, with the layout at the west end in view. The diagram above Tarek's hand does not show the full extent of the siding commissioned in May 2017.

MAIDENHEAD On 23 March 2016 the Kirow crane stands on the line that led to the former goods yard while laying out new sections of pointwork. The Bourne End branch curves off to the right, while behind the crane are the site offices where staff were based for works in this area; this later became the site of the EMU holding sidings. The work at this location took place over several years, when large windows of opportunity existed (generally Easter and Christmas) to install new pointwork, revise the track layout and install new OLE.

MAIDENHEAD This community engagement event for the Crossrail works on Easter Sunday 2016 highlighted the forthcoming work that was to be undertaken and the benefits of the Crossrail programme when complete.

MAIDENHEAD By October 2016 the masts for the new OLE had reached the station, seen in this view as a Class 165 unit draws to a stand on the 16th. The new canopies are evident on both platforms, installed as part of the Crossrail works.

MAIDENHEAD Looking in the opposite direction on the same day, when the author gave a safety briefing at Maidenhead, this picture shows the extent of the mast erection. This was undertaken by Balfour Beatty working under the direction of Network Rail, achieving some high productivity rates and completed the wiring ahead of the original schedule in May 2017, against a June date.

MAIDENHEAD On the early morning of Boxing Day 2016, looking towards Reading after a cold night, the new layout is in situ leading into the new stabling sidings built for Crossrail EMUs. These were used on an interim basis for the EMU-operated GWR service from Paddington to Maidenhead introduced in May 2017. The Kirow crane on the left is continuing its work laying out new track sections. The Bourne End branch is seen curving off to the right.

MAIDENHEAD On the night of Boxing Day 2016 a train of box wagons, to be loaded with spent ballast, stands on the Up Main line, on the London side of Maidenhead station, as an excavator clears the trackbed for installation of new trackwork in one of the final blockades to finalise the new track and signal layout at this location.

MAIDENHEAD That same night this is Platform 5, showing the new platform fascia and track being laid ready to receive the Class 345 EMUs. The OLE equipment had been installed earlier, before which the historic wooden train shed was donated to the Cholsey & Walllingford Railway; it is now being restored with the help of a Railway Heritage Associate grant for re-erection at Wallingford.

MAIDENHEAD On Christmas Day 2016, looking towards Reading at the country end of the station, the new track formation is going in before track and point laying takes place. Adjacent on the left is a rake of 'Salmon' wagons loaded with the old track sections. Note that the staff are wearing dust masks to protect against silica dust from the track ballast. To the right of the dozer is where Network Rail installed new EMU stabling sidings on the site of the old goods yard.

MAIDENHEAD 22 May 2017 was a proud day for Network Rail and GWR. The 09.10 Paddington to Maidenhead service was the first timetabled electrically operated passenger train to Maidenhead and it is seen here arriving.

MAIDENHEAD This view, looking in the opposite direction on the same day, shows the full extent of the electrification in the Maidenhead station area. These smart four-car trains replaced two- and three-car DMUs.

MAIDENHEAD On 23 June 2017 the first empty stock train burst through the banner marking the opening of the new stabling sidings. The sidings are intended for Crossrail trains but under an interim arrangement were initially used to stable GWR Class 387 EMUs.

2. Reading and Didcot

Reading saw the most changes to the track and signal layout in a scheme that had been under development from the early 2000s to deal with the rise in the volume of freight and passenger traffic. When the scheme was originally conceived it was expected to take six years to execute and cost just under £900 million. The scheme provided a new track layout, three diveunders and additional platforms as well as modifications to and lengthening of some of the existing ones.

The changes at Reading are almost a single symbol of the whole transformation of the region. Before 2010 Reading station had flat junctions at either end, limited narrow platforms largely furnished with GWR canopies and buildings, a 1989/90 footbridge

READING Before the start of work in 2008, the author's colleague Rob Mashford had the foresight to capture the scene at Reading station before works commenced. In the middle at the bottom with the white roof is the former Post Office building, which became the Reading Redevelopment Office. Centre middle is the former Reading Panel Signal Box, closed at Christmas 2010 as the land it occupied was required for new track formations and platforms. Also evident is the footbridge on the left, at the London end of the station layout.

and some station forecourt development. Starting at Christmas 2010 the Reading scheme changed all this, concluding in 2015 and providing:

- Additional and lengthened platforms
- A reinstated diveunder line at the east end of the station
- The construction of a mile-long viaduct for the Fast lines allowing two diveunder lines
- The construction of a new traincare depot
- A new chord line within the existing Reading triangle to allow east-to-west rail movements

The electrification was continued beyond Maidenhead to Didcot, going live on 28 December 2017, and platform extensions have also been made between Reading and Didcot. Didcot station itself also saw changes in the form of lengthened platforms and a new footbridge built by Network Rail linking it to a new multi-storey car park built by GWR.

The electrification works were continued beyond Didcot and went live through to Swindon (actually Wotton Bassett Junction) on 28 June 2018.

READING Looking towards Bristol in April 2012, this was the view along the old Platform 4, which has now been widened and renumbered Platform 7. In the distance is the old bay platform, yet to be reconfigured and fitted with new canopies. The transfer deck was edged in over the operational railway.

READING This April 2012 view is from the old footbridge, which was installed with the enhancements of the late 1980s and subsequently removed. Evident is the progress on the new transfer deck.

READING A year later the track and platforms seen in the previous photograph are complete and awaiting commissioning.

READING On 22 August 2013 the author caught DB Cargo No 59202 hauling MBA 'Monster' box wagons returning from Acton Yard to Westbury as it passed through Reading station. The newly laid line to the left of the train will become the new Platform 7 line, and where the locomotive is passing now forms the widened Platform 7 surface.

READING 17 July 2014 was a special day for the railway industry and the town of Reading with HM the Queen officially opening the new station. Invited guests included Reading Council and the Train Operating Companies GWR and CrossCountry, which had supported Network Rail with the scheme, while the Council had been a great advocate for it. Here Network Rail Project Director Bill Henry looks on next to the newly named HOPs machine, named moments earlier by Her Majesty.

READING The author, perspiring lightly, meets Her Majesty the Queen. After introductions, Her Majesty had a briefing on the Network Rail works across the region, and showed great interest in the planned rail link to Heathrow and rail growth in the Bristol area.

READING An hour after the Queen's visit the HOPS machine was still in the platform awaiting its return to its stabling depot at Swindon, in the former down-side yard.

READING On 27 December 2014, looking east towards the station, a Colas Class 70 loco stands with a rake of DB Cargo 'Coalfish' four-wheel wagons as Carillion staff press on with the new formation works. On the right remote-controlled Network Rail side-tipper wagons wait to discharge fresh ballast.

READING Three days later the reconfigured layout at the Bristol end of the station is making good progress as final sweeping of track fittings and sleepers occurs.

Above: **READING** On Easter Saturday 2015, with the station bereft of passengers, DB Cargo's No 66148 head towards the west end with empty bogie box wagons for loading with spent ballast. The author caught this shot while heading to grab some lunch when he and colleagues worked away from home for over a week during this extraordinary blockade, when £16 million worth of work was undertaken, concluding with the full track and signalling layout being commissioned.

Above right: **READING** A large-scale bus operation was operated by GWR during the Easter 2015 blockade, which stretched from Maidenhead to Didcot. The revised forecourt area was a part of Network Rail's redevelopment of the station and became a legacy benefit with a road-rail transfer point that had never previously existed – the site was originally part of the Reading Signalling Works – contrast with the aerial photograph taken in 2008.

READING The author and his colleagues realised that eyes were watching the major works that Easter, especially after the awful headline-making news items at Christmas 2014 with possession over-runs on the Paddington-Reading corridor and the south end of the East Coast Main Line. This view shows a DB Cargo re-rerailing vehicle, which was hired in case problems arose. Fortunately it wasn't required, and the whole possession was handed back on time, with no accidents or incidents and all works executed as expected., after 97,000 hours worked by 1000 people.

READING The Easter 2015 blockade saw much use made of the Kirow crane to lay out track and pointwork for installation. On a beautiful Easter Sunday at the west (country) end of the station Rob Mashford captured this scene of the crane laying out the pointwork by the start of the flyover.

READING Where new infrastructure is introduced – be that new signalled track layouts, timetables or in this case gradients – modelling work has to involve train operators. The men and women of the Reading project team (engineers and project managers) worked with the railfreight companies when designing the Reading viaduct. While it was an absolute requirement that high-speed trains could deal with the viaduct gradients, it was also critical that Class 66 and 59 freight locomotives could do the same with loaded freight trains. The outcome of that work for Reading is seen in this image.

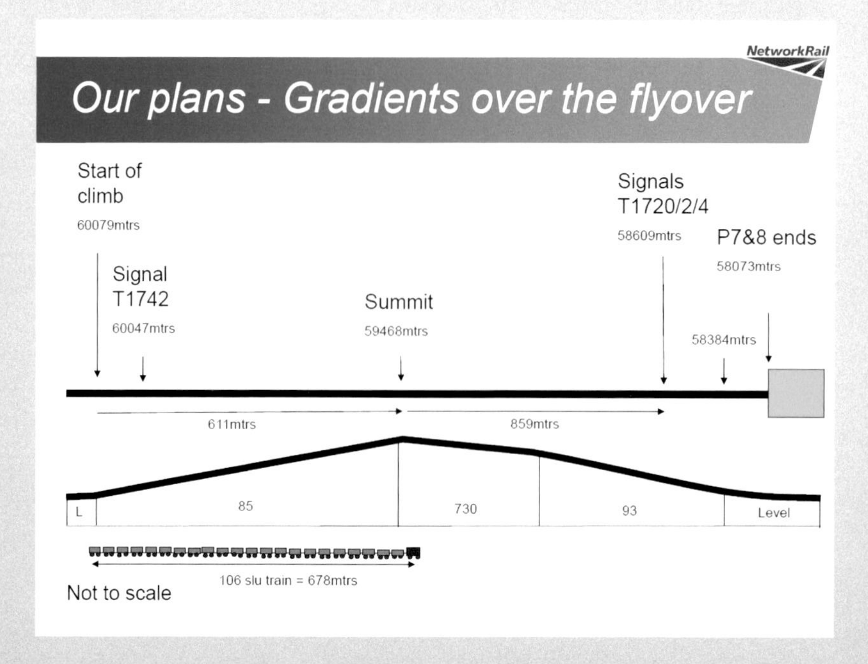

Right: **READING** At the west end of the layout the Kirow crane travels toward the station with a spreader beam ready to lift the next new track section.

Main image: **READING** The first train to pass over the new viaduct on 3 January 2015 is captured as it heads southbound.

READING Viewed from the new viaduct on Good Friday 2015, a Freightliner Heavy Haul Class 66 loco brings a materials train around to the blockade worksite, formed of tilting wagons loaded with new pointwork, auto-ballaster hopper wagons and 'Salmon' bogie flat wagons, used to convey track sections.

Above: **READING** Seen in the early hours of Easter Saturday 2015 is the Network Rail Gold Control Room for the Reading works with, left to right, Matt Heywood (seated), then Andy Dutton, who authored the rail industry contingency plan supporting the Reading Easter Works. Also seated are Project Director Reading Bill Henry from Bechtel and Mike Hogg, GWR's Interface Director. Standing is Julian Burnell, Network Rail communications manager, then seated is Robbie Burns, Regional Director, and finally Andy Spencer. Through the life of the programme Andy Spencer was key in planning works, and Mike Hogg was a great supporter. Out of shot were Tim Leighton and Bryan Keetch, who were also tracking the Slough resignalling works that were ongoing at the same time as the Reading block. This meant that new signalling interfaces had to be established between two resignallings that were happening at the same time. At the end of Easter blockade, a GWR Class 150 DMU went round the whole of the newly commissioned layout to establish that it all worked correctly, and an interesting hour ensued as the Thames Valley Signallers sent the train over every conceivable signalled route at 03.00 before the 03.48 Reading to Paddington service, the first train, left from Platform 15.

Left: **READING** 6 April 2015 saw the final big push to complete the final new Reading layout before its commissioning a few days later. The DB Cargo Class 66 loco is standing at the head of auto-ballaster wagons alongside the viaduct, which now has OLE masts attached. The small rail-wheeled units nearest the camera are remote-controlled and work in tandem with one another to move trackwork.

Top left: **READING** from the air. A month after the new layout opened, in May 2015, Rob Mashford arranged to secure aerial photographs of the completed layout. This view shows the Westbury end of the layout. The line curving at the bottom left passes over the site of the old Reading DMU depot; this double-track route is so useful to signallers and train planners for services to and from the Mendip quarries, passing under the new viaduct, construction of which had started in 2013 after the old DMU depot was vacated.

Bottom left: **READING** This second May 2015 aerial view is looking towards Didcot, and the full extent of the triangle layout is evident, together with the new train-care depot to the right of the running lines that form the core London to Bristol main line. The Berks & Hants route is to the left of the picture, heading toward Southcote Junction.

Above: **READING** A DB Cargo freight train, conveying empty car-carrying wagons from Southampton Docks to Didcot, is captured in May 2015 heading under the Fast lines, which are the core main line to and from Swindon. Before the flyover and diverunders were constructed at the west end of the station, Reading signallers would have to find an 8-minute gap between trains on the Reading-Swindon and Reading-Basingstoke routes to weave a freight train across the flat junction.

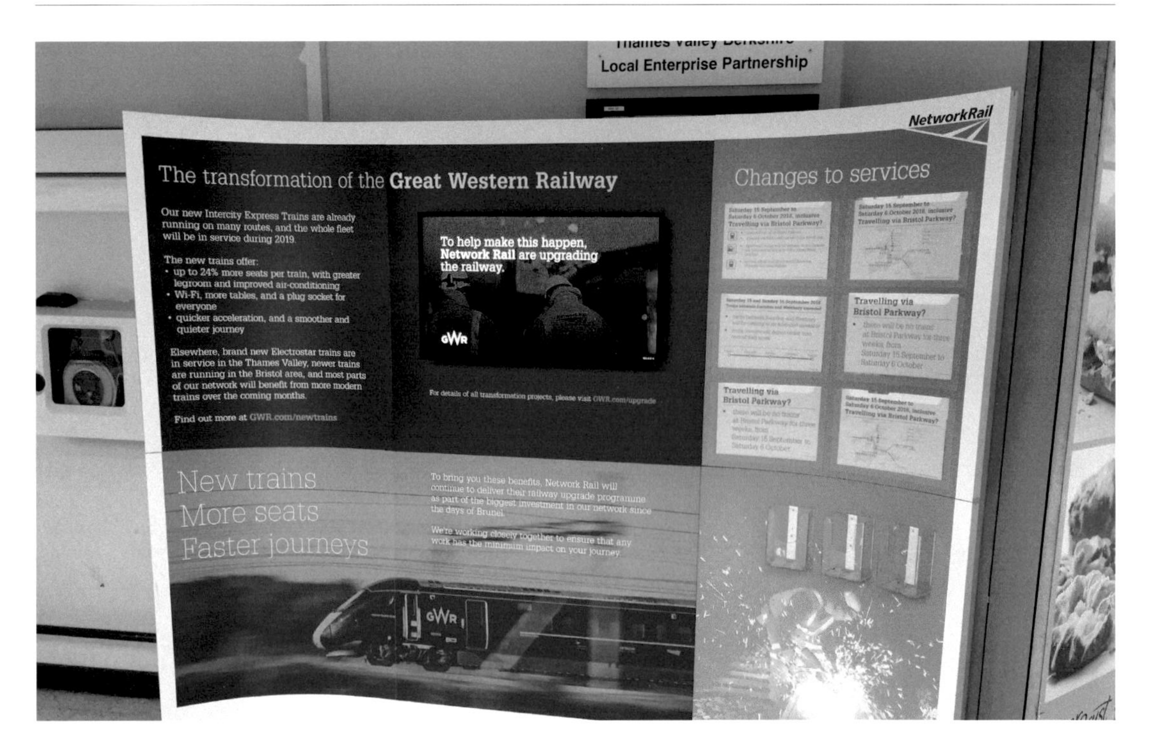

READING These two GWR posters on Reading station in August 2018 give a snapshot of the scale of the works (and the impact on rail users) when large-scale works take place to install, commission and test new OLE equipment.

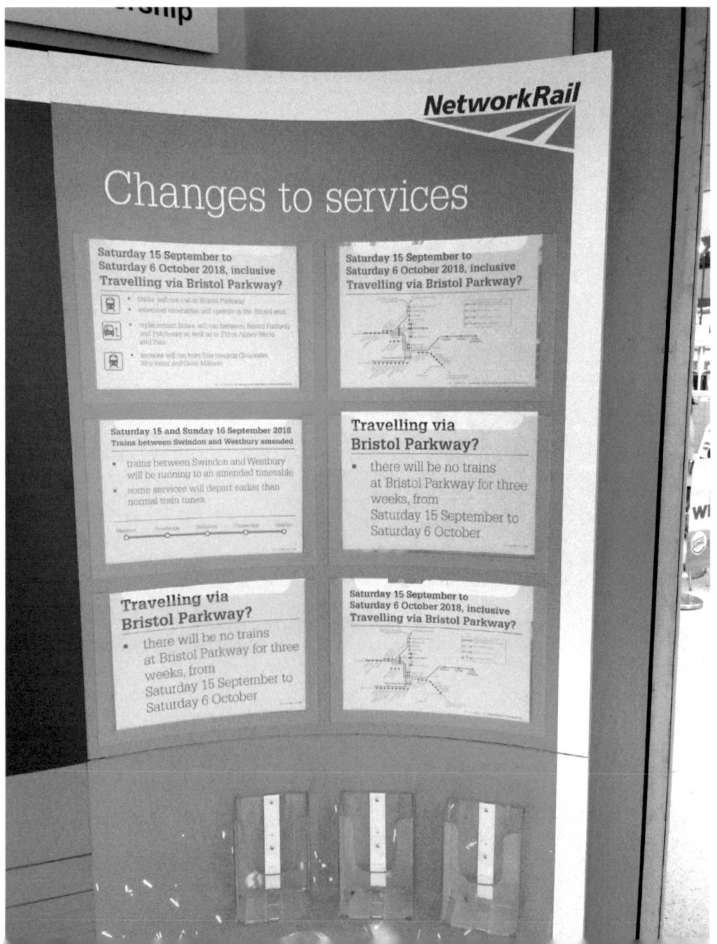

Left: **PANGBOURNE** On 17 June 2016 *Flying Scotsman* heads a Holyhead to Paddington charter train and becomes the oldest main-line steam engine to travel under what was then the UK's newest OLE installation. The section through Pangbourne formed the test track section between Didcot and Reading.

Below: **DIDCOT** Concomitant with the Reading blockade was the large-scale renewal of points and crossings at Moreton Cutting, just east of Didcot station, seen here on Easter Sunday 2015 during a weekend that was aided by fine weather. A key imperative was to renew all nine points at this location before the erection of the overhead wires.

DIDCOT Taken between Moreton Cutting and the station, this July 2017 picture shows the height differential between container wagons to good effect, together with the OLE automatic wire tensioning system. To allow high-gauge containers Network Rail gauge cleared Southampton/Oxford/Birmingham in 2011.

DIDCOT On Easter Sunday 2013 the author was a volunteer at Didcot station with GWR colleagues as GWR and CrossCountry trains were terminating there while upgrade work on the Didcot to Reading section progressed. CrossCountry operated buses from Didcot to Winchester during this weekend. Here an HST stands at the possession limit boards.

DIDCOT Christmas Day 2015 was one of a few days notable for very high winds, at a time when a huge volume of upgrade works was taking place across the region from East London (as part of the Crossrail programme) through to the Exeter Signalling Centre. This sunny view at the east end of Didcot belies the high winds with which the staff had to contend as masts swung and had to be controlled.

DIDCOT At the west end of the station a road crane stands in GWR's station car park to lower an OLE boom into position on the Relief line. Later on Christmas Day the works had to be aborted as staff wrestled to control the booms in the strong winds as they were lifted by the road crane. In about 20 minutes GWR's Barry Milson generously resolved to leave the booms in the station car park after a call from the author.

DIDCOT On 10 October 2017 the author caught a Class 800 unit on test as he travelled on an inspection special that was momentarily stationary in Didcot station. Less than a week later the 800 Class entered passenger service. Ready for autumn on the right-hand side is the railhead treatment train.

DIDCOT Another boom installation continues on Christmas Day 2015. In the distance is the temporary footbridge from the station to the car park; this was replaced in the summer of 2018 by a new permanent structure (see next page).

Rachel Pitt, Local Operations Manager, Thames Valley Signalling Centre, Didcot

I joined the railway in September 2014, on the Network Rail General Management Graduate Scheme, and straight away was overwhelmed by the vast level of work that was ongoing, the phenomenal number of projects and people who were dedicated to improving the railway for the millions of people who travel across the route every year. I spent my first three months getting very familiar with the real challenge that are leaves on the line, and immersing myself into an entire arm of the business dedicated to reducing the impact that the seasons have on train performance. I was then offered the chance to spend my Christmas with Infrastructure Projects, and was able to witness the demolition of two bridges to enable the installation of overhead wires. I spent time with engineers, who patiently explained the proposed track design for Maidenhead siding, and every single person I spoke to had a clear sense of excitement for the future.

I finally took my first permanent role working within the Operations team as a Local Operations Manager at Didcot and was able to start to understand the real day-to-day challenges that were introduced through these improvements and developments. From the gauging restrictions on the new trains testing on the network, to the training surrounding the introduction of overhead wires to a new area for signallers and electrical control room operators. The requirements to be running trains and ensuring performance focus, while still maximising the access available for both day-to-day maintenance and project delivery work, is significant. The number of people involved in any successful project delivery never fails to surprise me, and the sense of pride throughout every facet of the industry after a successful delivery is something quite exceptional to witness.

DIDCOT By March 2018 the operation of electric trains to Didcot was well established, as evidenced by this shot of No 387168 forming a local service to London as an HST bound for Bristol enters the station. The works on the left-hand side are associated with the station platform extension.

Right and top of opposite page: **DIDCOT** A new footbridge was erected at the south end of the station, linking to a new multi-storey car park constructed by GWR; the ramp starts adjacent to the down station platform, providing access for all. The bridge was installed over the second weekend of September 2018, involving the isolation of the live wires. It was landed successfully and final fitting out then occurred. On 28 December 2017, just before 16.00, the first electric passenger train operated, with a GWR Class 387.

Below: **STRATTON** lies east of Swindon, and this 2015 scene typifies electrification work before mast erection commences, whereby bridges need to be rebuilt to allow sufficient wire clearance for the OLE. Forty-three bridges were rebuilt as part of electrifying from Maidenhead to Cardiff. This structure was a straightforward replacement, but nevertheless required a formal road closure and an all-lines-blocked possession on the Great Western Main Line. A common solution for bridge rebuilds adopted during the programme was to retain the lower elements of the structure and place a new concrete beam and upper abutments to give enhanced clearances.

3. Swindon

Mark Langman, Route Managing Director, Western Route, Network Rail

On Christmas Day 2016 Route Managing Director Mark Langman (right) and former Infrastructure Projects Regional Director Robbie Burns break for a photo during the huge suite of works at Maidenhead to install the final track and signal layout ready for the May 2017 timetable.

During your journey through this book, you have now arrived at Swindon, historic and proud railway town and home to the Network Rail Western Route.

The Great Western Main Line is undergoing its most significant upgrade since it was built by Brunel over 175 years ago, and Paul's book reflects the scale of that work.

By the end of the investment period 2014 to 2019, Network Rail will have electrified the route from Paddington to Reading, Bristol to Cardiff and from Reading to Newbury, modernised signalling and infrastructure, and enabled the biggest train fleet upgrade in a modern generation benefiting passengers across the whole route.

When the work is complete, passengers will benefit from the introduction of a new timetable that, combined with the new trains already delivered, will further improve their journeys, providing more services with more seats, faster journey times and new connections. That process started in the autumn of 2017 when GWR introduced its Inter-city Express Trains, and continued with the introduction of the new Thames Valley electric timetable in January 2018, using new Class 387 'Electrostar' trains.

This has been a tremendous achievement and is the result of unprecedented levels of public investment from Government; the support of our customers, the train and freight operators; and of course passengers, lineside residents and businesses across the region.

Railway staff have played their part too, faced with a difficult challenge of running and maintaining a busy railway over the past eight years, which have seen unprecedented levels of investment and engineering work delivered.

This book is a tribute to the dedication of railway men and railway women and the legacy they leave to better the railway for the communities and industries they serve.

Left and above: **SWINDON** The middle point of the line became the home for the High-Output Electrification Train, which was ordered in 2012 and built by Windhoff in Germany. Network Rail Electrification Manager Matt Swancott photographed the train upon arrival at its new home in Swindon Transfer Sidings. Operated by Amey, it was a piece of new equipment of an unknown quantity and initially had an unfair bad reputation. However, as the train and its team bedded in, high-volume activity commenced and began to set records. The train has multiple parts to enable pile excavations, pile insertion, mast erection and small part steel erection. Additionally it can undertake wiring runs. It is also equipped with a pantograph and can test newly erected overhead wires.

SWINDON In Swindon's Cocklebury Sidings on the up side of the line is a new electrification train school, which was formally opened on 27 May 2016, as witnessed in this photograph. The school has classrooms and practical examples of OLE equipment outdoors to train Network Rail staff in the art of maintenance of an overhead wire system.

SWINDON On Christmas Eve 2015 the setting sun highlights seven Class 66 locomotives heading to Oxford to work trains for that period's works. That Christmas no fewer than 57 logistics trains worked west of Paddington.

SWINDON This 2014 view shows the station before resignalling and electrification work commenced, as the focus was on the Reading area rebuild and Crossrail works on the GW Main Line. In this view up and down GWR HSTs frame a DB Cargo Class 66 loco as it rests between shunting the steel terminal west of the station, opened in 2008. This scene has been totally transformed since resignalling and electrification.

SWINDON Taken from the same position, this June 2017 scene reveals an East Coast 'Azuma' train on test on the Great Western Main Line, as gauge clearance had already been established on the route for this type of train. Since the date of the last photograph, Swindon resignalling has taken place, highlighted by the change in signal type.

SWINDON Adjacent to the Platform 1 line at Swindon is the freight line to the steel depot. Under the wires on 9 August 2018 a DB Cargo Class 66 loco sets back into the terminal.

SWINDON A GWR train to Cheltenham awaits departure from the bay platform in January 2013. At that time the resignalling of Swindon was being planned, having originally been scheduled for December 2013; it was consciously delayed to give precedence to the early stages of the Victoria resignalling, as the forward planning evidence highlighted a risk to works through a shortage of signal commissioning staff.

SWINDON The rate of change is evident from these two photographs, with little over a year separating new-build Peppercorn 'Pacific' *Tornado* heading a St David's Day special to Cardiff on 1 March 2017 and the scene in July 2018, transformed by the erection of masts and wires as a DB Cargo aggregates train heads for Whatley Quarry, diverted because of a block on the Newbury line for electrification work.

SWINDON On a sunny Saturday morning, 26 September 1987, the author caught 7Z10, a Severn Tunnel Junction to Swindon train, approaching its destination with 'Dogfish' ballast wagons for weekend engineering work. These wagons were vacuum-braked and had disappeared by the 1990s as investment was made in modern high-capacity ballast wagons of the type seen in the works at Reading.

SWINDON At the same location just over 30 years later in July 2018, a GWR Class 57 locomotive on empty sleeping car stock draws into the station. The OLE booms were erected over Christmas 2017 and wiring followed. Behind the locomotive is a Bulk Electricity Supply Point; these exist at regular intervals along the main line to feed the OLE system.

SWINDON During snowfall in the spring of 2018 a GWR HST, named *Sir Kenneth Grange* after the train's designer, enters the station under recently erected booms. They had been erected during the Christmas 2017 possession when the 'all lines blocked' afforded the chance to install these huge booms, which had to span multiple lines. Additionally seen here is the work on Platforms 1 and 3 to install new energy-efficient LED lights.

SWINDON The High-Output Electrification Train stands on the through line in March 2017. This photograph was taken to emphasise how the steel shields are able to protect people and trains when an adjacent rail line is open to rail traffic as electrification work takes place.

Top: **SWINDON** In the wake of the Christmas 2017 blockade, and the large-scale erection of masts around Swindon, came the installation of wiring runs, after the installation of small-part steel fittings and insulators. A wire run is 1,300 metres long and can be carried on the High-Output Electrification Train. The regular Westbury-Oxford materials train – supporting upgrade and renewal works – passes through the station at some speed; in contrast to the ballast hopper wagons seen on page <??> these are high-capacity with an 80-tonne carrying capacity. The photo shows to good effect the new signals installed as part of the Swindon resignalling of the previous year.

Middle: **SWINDON** Weekends during the summer of 2018 saw regular blockades of the line between Bristol Temple Meads and Filton Abbey Wood, necessitating diversions via Bath, Swindon (reverse) and Stroud for CrossCountry trains. Here the 11.00 Bristol to Newcastle service reverses on Sunday 8 July 2018.

Bottom: **SWINDON** The GW Main Line is not solely the preserve of GWR as train operator, with CrossCountry, Freightliner, DB Cargo and GB Railfreight operating daily trains. The latter operator is seen here, with a train of armoured personnel vehicles from Warminster to Donnington, also on 8 July 2018, keeping loads off the roads. A year earlier there were no masts or wires and signalling had recently just been recontrolled from Swindon A signal box to the Thames Valley Signalling Centre.

4. Wootton Bassett Junction to Bath Spa

On this two-track railway a number of works took place to transform the line. Electrification to Chippenham was completed in August 2018, following extensive track lowering near Brinkworth in 2017 and an underbridge rebuild to allow sufficient space for wires to pass under an adjacent overbridge. Additionally, a new access-for-all footbridge with lifts was built at Chippenham station, opening on 22 January 2016.

Signalling in the area was recontrolled to Didcot in 2016 with the closure of Swindon A signal box.

The track through Box Tunnel was lowered in 2015 and major tunnel drainage works undertaken. Moving further west, Bath Spa saw reconfigured lines through the station, a new platform fascia and extended platforms. There were also extensive pointwork renewals at Bathampton Junction in the summer of 2015 and around Bath Goods in the spring of 2016.

WOOTTON BASSETT JUNCTION Bridge reconstruction started in 2014 on the Swindon to Bristol Parkway route and this photograph shows the demolition of a bridge on May Bank Holiday 2016, before replacement with a new centre structure to give sufficient OLE clearance. The excavator is standing on the main running lines, which are covered with protective boarding. By the summer of 2018 the masts and wires were complete through this location.

WOOTTON BASSETT JUNCTION Artist Ian Cryer – who is also a DB Cargo ground staff member – captured this scene in 2018 showing the Wootton Bassett Stone Terminal with a Class 59-hauked train unloading its stone, the local Westbury-Swindon passenger train, and the 16.00 Paddington-Bristol train. The wires through the junction here were erected from 2017 onwards.

CHRISTIAN MALFORD is between Wootton Bassett and Chippenham. With both lines out, the underpass (culvert) here was lowered, which then enabled the track to be lowered to gain sufficient clearance under a brick arch overbridge for the OLE. In this view the 360 excavator prepares to lay a bed of sand in the excavated culvert. Culverts are structures that are often unseen by rail users, but essential to the safe operation of the railway by allowing water to move between land on either side.

CHRISTIAN MALFORD The summer of 2017 saw a midweek blockade to work at multiple locations on the Wootton Bassett to Chippenham line, including lowering track – see the previous photo – linked to installation of OLE, and erecting OLE masts. During the block GWR services and freight services operated via the Hullavington line. In this view road-railers are engaged in mast installation. After Christmas 2017 OLE wire installation took place, which was completed to Chippenham by August 2018.

CHRISTIAN MALFORD During that same summer blockade, but several miles closer to Chippenham, two road-railers move to their next worksite, having erected the cross-boom. A site compound with road-rail machine access existed on the Swindon side of Chippenham, where materials were also stored. The concept of multiple loading points, without the expensive need for track and signalling, meant that, without too much transit time, machinery and people could get to a worksite quickly.

Network Rail

All the High Voltage equipment within Thingley Junction AutoTransformer Feeder Station (MLN1 96m 10ch) and the 25kV feeder cable, installed within a trough route in the cess, from Thingley Junction AutoTransformer Feeder Station to Royal Wootton Bassett AutoTransformer Feeder Station (MLN1 83m 04ch)

WARNING

The new Overhead line Equipment at this location shall be energised at

25,000 Volts AC

and must be considered LIVE and DANGEROUS

From 10:00 hours on Friday 29th June 2018

With immediate effect, if additional information is required please contact one of the following:-

David Blakeley
Programme Manager
Network Rail
SN1
Station Road
Swindon, SN1 1DG
Mob: 07973 411229
Email:david blakeley2@networkrail.co.uk

Chris Wilson
Programme Engineering Manager
Network Rail
SN1
Station Road
Swindon, SN1 1DG
Mob: 07786 338680
Email: chris.wilson@networkrail.co.uk

Didcot Electrical Control
British Telecom: 0330 8541051
Railway ETD: 085 41051
Emergency ETD: 085 41050
Emergency BT: 0330 8541050
Short Code: 170

By August 2018 the OLE construction was complete between Wootton Bassett Junction and Chippenham and powered up. It was essential therefore that staff were advised.

LANGLEY BURRELL On 16 February 2018 the 16.30 Bristol West Depot to Tilbury Freightliner train powers past Langley Burrell, just east of Chippenham, in a shot that the author panned. The train will now face the steep gradient up Dauntsey towards Wootton Bassett Junction. Bristol West freight terminal was reactivated in the summer of 2010 after 20 years of disuse. The installed masts are evident and carefully inspection will also reveal the power supply for the electric feeder station.

CHIPPENHAM On the night of 31 January 2015 a road crane occupies Chippenham station car park, on the site of the old goods yard, ready to lift out the old grey steel bridge, to be replaced by an access-for-all lift bridge, which opened a year later. The new bridge benefited people with cases, buggies and wheelchairs, and allowed the abolition of a barrow crossing at the west end of the station, making the railway safer and improving the journey experience.

CHIPPENHAM The following day, 1 February 2015, the bridge had gone, the railway reopened on time, and construction of the new structure started. As well as completing the possession of the railway, the car park was handing back to train operator GWR to minimise passenger disruption.

CHIPPENHAM In March 2018 the HOPS train waits to exit a possession between Wootton Bassett Junction and Chippenham as a GWR Class 165 unit operates a shuttle train between Chippenham and Bristol. The HOPS machine had been engaged in the installation of the wire run small-part steel items.

BATH SPA April 2017 saw a large blockade to relay lines through Bath Spa station, which would enable future electrification, improve the step distance and generate gauge clearance for new trains. This work took place over several weeks and pushed the concept of adjacent line open working to minimise impact on rail users while allowing the work to go ahead. The platform faces were moved out from their longstanding locations; the work involved the use of polystyrene blocks, onto which a brick fascia and new surface slabs were applied. The down line was first treated, then the up line was addressed, as seen here. There had been a major blockade in this area a year earlier in 2016 to relay multiple sets of pointwork at the west end of the station and to undertake a relay through Keynsham station.

5. Bristol Temple Meads to Penzance

This largely two-track section of railway remains as it has for some time, with the existing signal boxes still controlling the line. However, some changes occurred during the period 2010 to 2018, summarised as follows:

- Gauge clearance for new and cascaded GWR trains
- The reopening of Bristol West Freightliner Depot in the summer of 2010
- Flood mitigation works north of Exeter
- Refurbishment of Whiteball Tunnel in 2014 (with a further suite of extensive works in 2019)
- Resilience works on the Dawlish-Teignmouth coastal section, with further works planned
- Track renewal works at multiple locations
- Platform extension at Totnes and a new access-for-all bridge
- Additional signalling south of Plymouth in 2018
- A mine-capping operation at Scorrier

BRISTOL TEMPLE MEADS This 8 August 2018 photograph gives just a hint of the large-scale resignalling that occurred during 2017 and was commissioned at Easter 2018. New signal heads and associated new lineside equipment give the game away as a CrossCountry Bristol-Manchester train departs. On the left is the Network Rail Plain Line Pattern Recognition Train. Notwithstanding the upgrade over the last eight years, trains such as this running regularly are key to maintaining the railway; Colas Class 67 No 67027 is the train engine.

BRISTOL TEMPLE MEADS In the summer of 2018, before the next phase of blockades, the publicity highlighting the work was in evidence together with the signage for rail replacement buses.

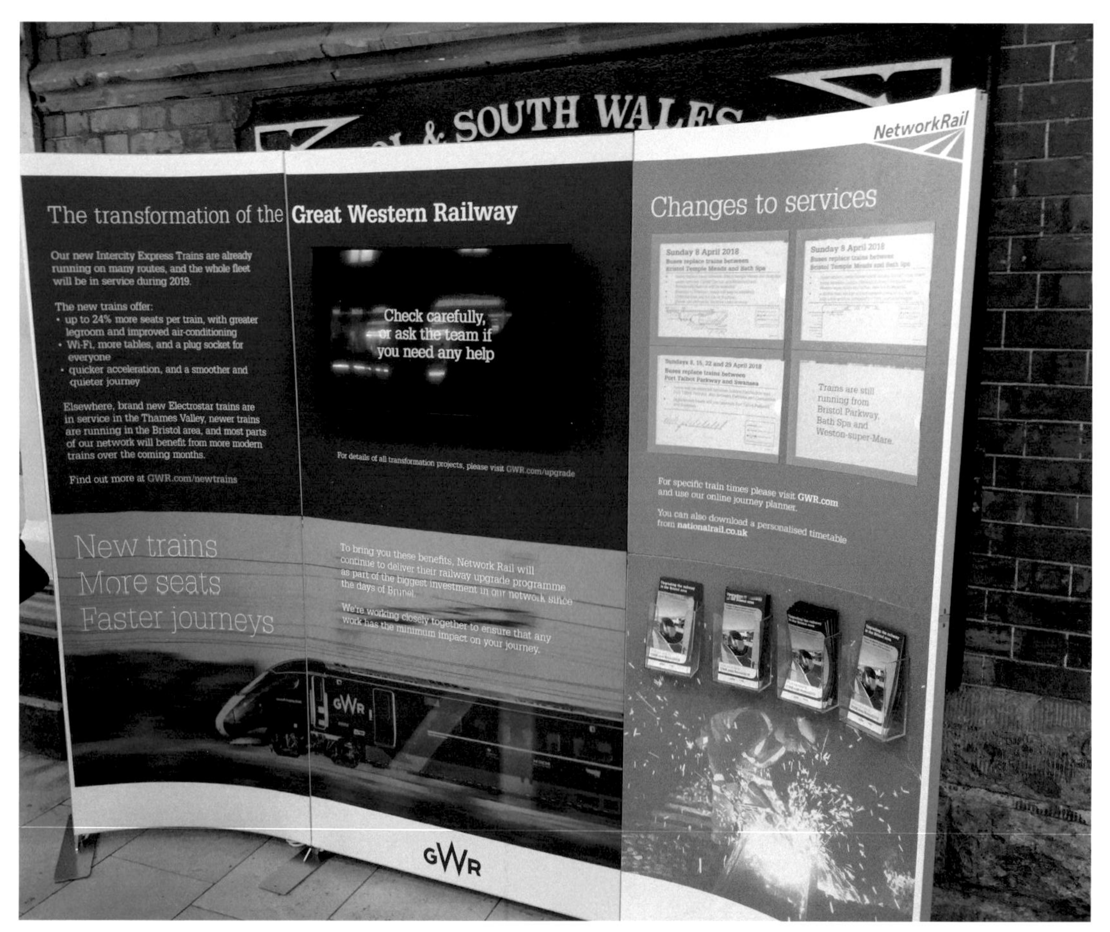

BRISTOL TEMPLE MEADS In a scene very different from today, this is the last day of locomotive-hauled trains between Cardiff and Portsmouth, on Sunday 15 May 1988. In those days trains ran about every 2 hours between the two cities, with Mark 1 coaches built in the 1950s and early '60s. This train is actually the service to Brighton. The workload for the Bristol signallers decreased after this day as the drivers of new Leyland two-car Class 155 DMUs simply changed cabs at Temple Meads, instead of having to uncouple and run round, or re-engine, the trains.

BRISTOL TEMPLE MEADS In November 1985 a 'Hastings' Class 33 locomotive runs into Bristol Bath Road depot, photographed by the author after he had finished a late shift at Bristol Travel Centre. This line was relaid in 2001 to give an additional platform (known as Platform 15) as Bristol area rail usage grew, then in 2018 Network Rail platform works took place to lengthen the platform for GWR IEP trains.

BRISTOL TEMPLE MEADS Two DRS Class 68 locomotives pass through the station with a freight service originating from Bridgwater heading for Crewe with wagons of nuclear fuel for reprocessing. Evident in this view is one of the new mid-platform signals commissioned at Easter 2018 when the Temple Meads area was resignalling and recontrolled to Thames Valley Signalling Centre. This resignalling was the largest that Network Rail had undertaken, and a real tribute to all the staff engaged in the work. In the second picture the train is seen at the north end of the station, transformed since the removal of the mail conveyor. The station roof is set to be transformed during 2020-21.

BRISTOL TEMPLE MEADS With Platforms 15 and 13 extended by the autumn of 2018, they were now capable of taking the new GWR ten- and nine-car trains. The ugly Royal Mail conveyor seen in photograph of the Class 33 locomotive was removed at Christmas 2015. The Royal Mail buildings were in use until 2000, dispatching and receiving railborne mail; the opening of the Mail Rail depot at Bristol Parkway and Royal Mail's move to Filton made this complex redundant. The redevelopment of the old Royal Mail building as a campus will serve to further regenerate this area. Also seen on the same day in March 2018 at the south end of Platforms 15 and 13 is an HST at rest, with the new extension evident.

BRISTOL TEMPLE MEADS The new LED signalling and speed limits of Easter 2018 are evident in this photograph looking towards London Paddington. In the background British Railways 'Merchant Navy' Class steam locomotive No 35028 *Clan Line* brings in Pullman cars to form a regular return service to London Victoria, which also called at Bath Spa to collect guests.

BRISTOL TEMPLE MEADS
The resignalling of the station was a complex piece of work and was successfully achieved over Easter 2018. The new Temple Meads area is best captured in these diagrams showing the newly resignalled station area.

Legend

Permanent Speed Restrictions
40
Advance
60
15 DMU 30
15

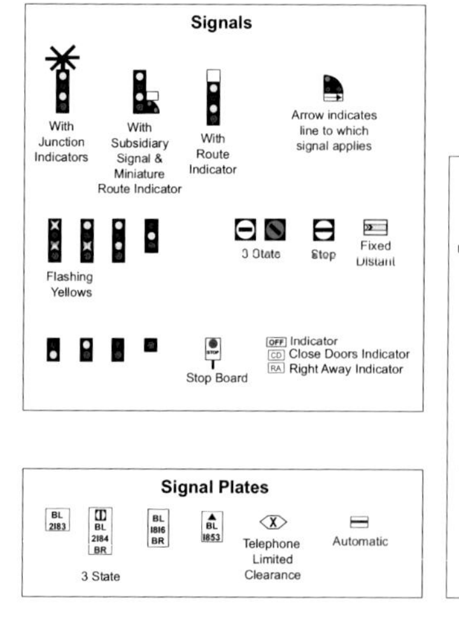

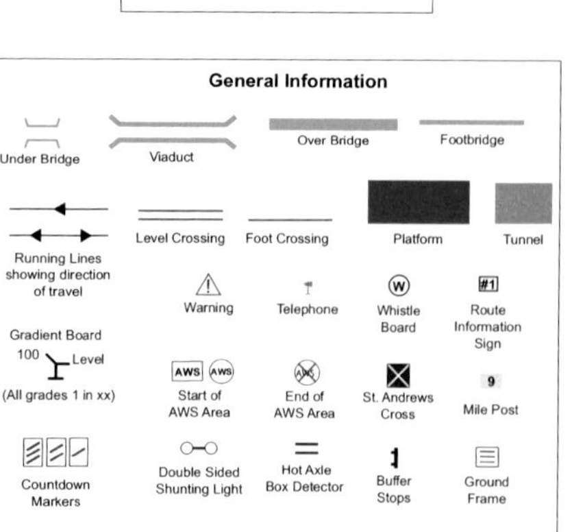

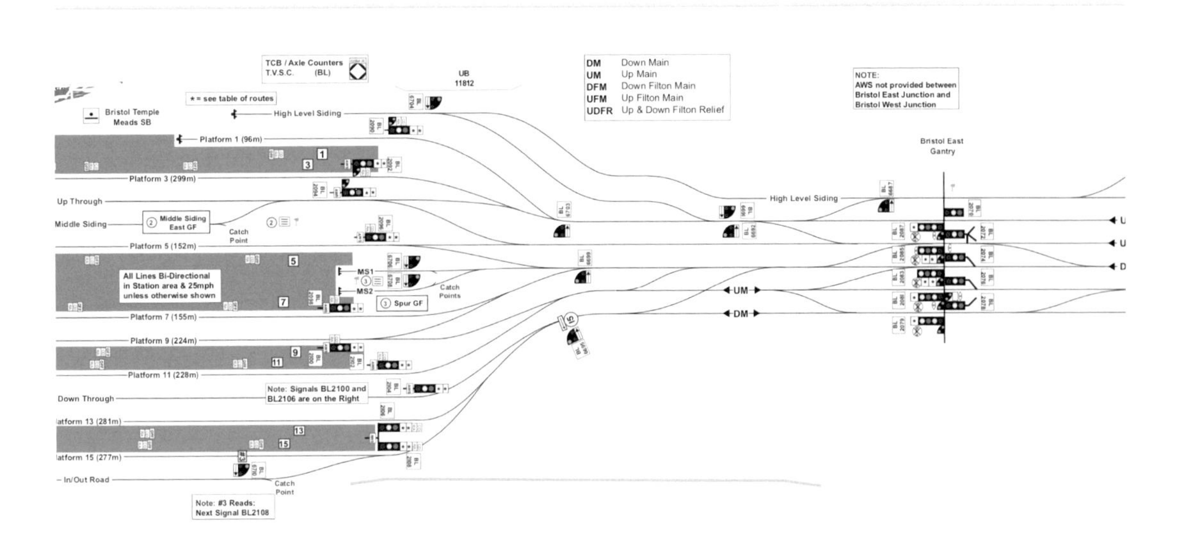
TCB / Axle Counters
T.V.S.C. (BL)
UB
11812
DM Down Main
UM Up Main
DFM Down Filton Main
UFM Up Filton Main
UDFR Up & Down Filton Relief
NOTE:
AWS not provided between Bristol East Junction and Bristol West Junction
Bristol East Gantry
Bristol Temple Meads SB
* = see table of routes
High Level Siding
Platform 1 (96m)
Platform 3 (299m)
Up Through
Middle Siding
Middle Siding East GF
Catch Point
Platform 5 (152m)
All Lines Bi-Directional in Station area & 25mph unless otherwise shown
MS1
MS2
Spur GF
Catch Points
Platform 7 (155m)
UM
DM
Platform 9 (224m)
Platform 11 (228m)
Down Through
Note: Signals BL2100 and BL2106 are on the Right
latform 13 (281m)
latform 15 (277m)
In/Out Road
Catch Point
Note: #3 Reads: Next Signal BL2108

NetworkRail

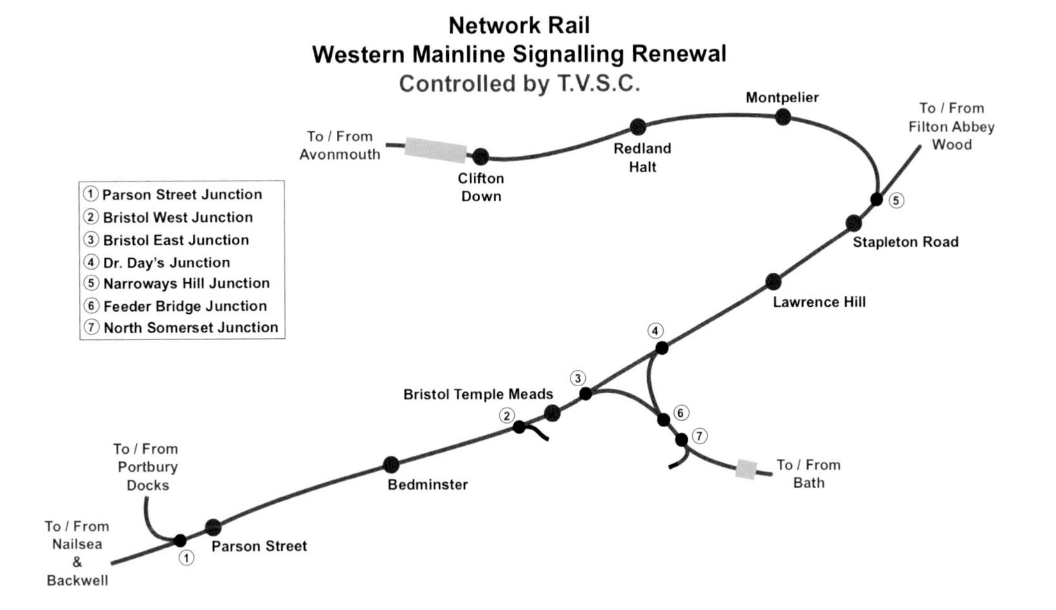
Network Rail
Western Mainline Signalling Renewal
Controlled by T.V.S.C.
1 Parson Street Junction
2 Bristol West Junction
3 Bristol East Junction
4 Dr. Day's Junction
5 Narroways Hill Junction
6 Feeder Bridge Junction
7 North Somerset Junction
To / From Avonmouth
Clifton Down
Redland Halt
Montpelier
To / From Filton Abbey Wood
Stapleton Road
Lawrence Hill
Bristol Temple Meads
Bedminster
To / From Bath
To / From Portbury Docks
To / From Nailsea & Backwell
Parson Street

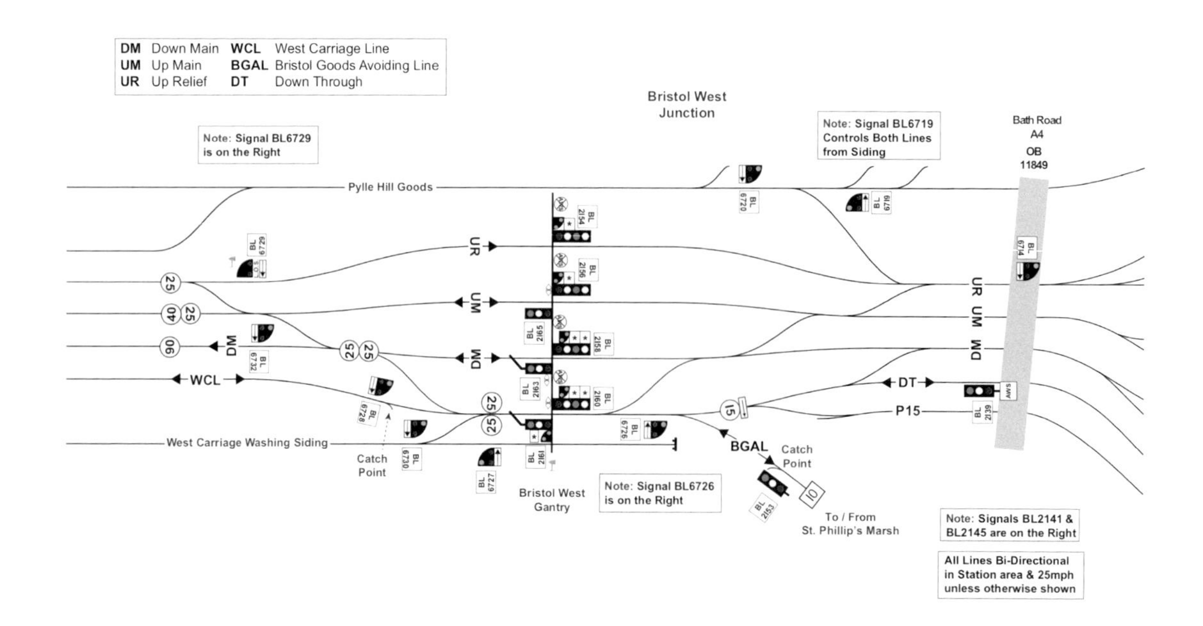
DM Down Main
UM Up Main
UR Up Relief
WCL West Carriage Line
BGAL Bristol Goods Avoiding Line
DT Down Through
Bristol West Junction
Note: Signal BL6729 is on the Right
Note: Signal BL6719 Controls Both Lines from Siding
Bath Road A4 OB 11849
Pylle Hill Goods
West Carriage Washing Siding
Catch Point
Bristol West Gantry
Note: Signal BL6726 is on the Right
BGAL
To / From St. Phillip's Marsh
Note: Signals BL2141 & BL2145 are on the Right
All Lines Bi-Directional in Station area & 25mph unless otherwise shown

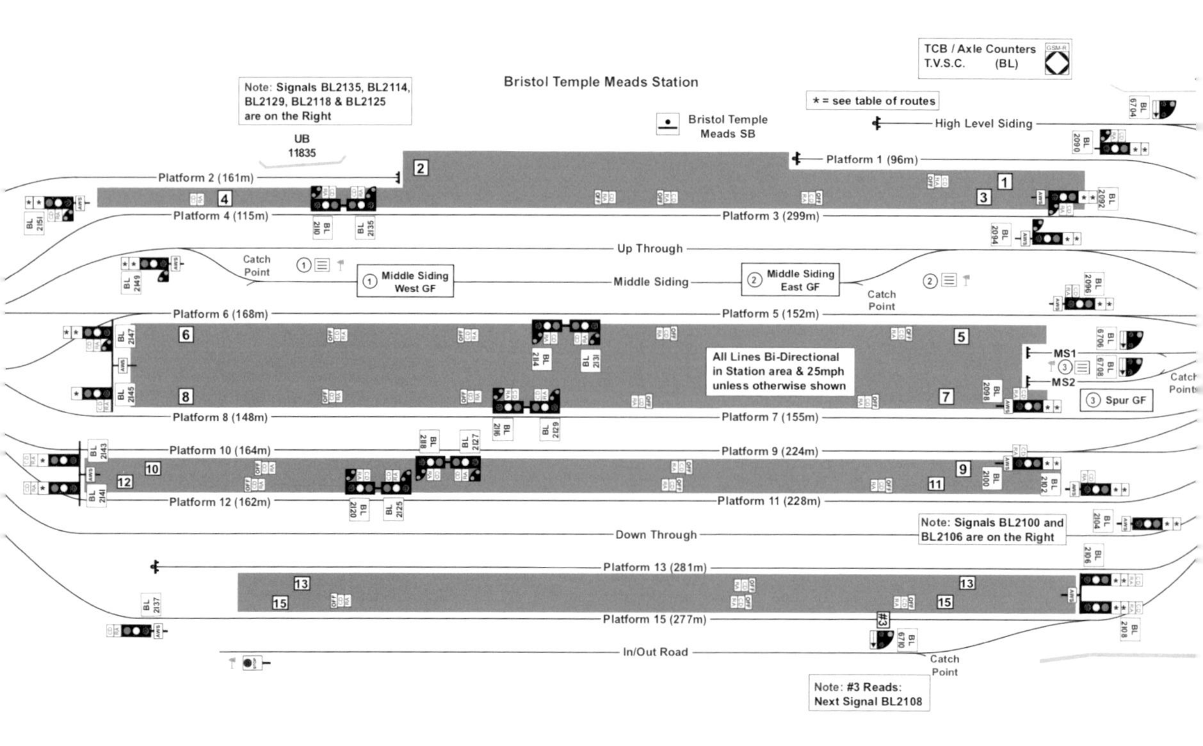
TCB / Axle Counters T.V.S.C. (BL)
Bristol Temple Meads Station
Note: Signals BL2135, BL2114, BL2129, BL2118 & BL2125 are on the Right
* = see table of routes
Bristol Temple Meads SB
High Level Siding
UB 11835
Platform 2 (161m)
Platform 1 (96m)
Platform 4 (115m)
Platform 3 (299m)
Up Through
Middle Siding West GF
Middle Siding
Middle Siding East GF
Platform 6 (168m)
Platform 5 (152m)
All Lines Bi-Directional in Station area & 25mph unless otherwise shown
Spur GF
Platform 8 (148m)
Platform 7 (155m)
Platform 10 (164m)
Platform 9 (224m)
Platform 12 (162m)
Platform 11 (228m)
Down Through
Note: Signals BL2100 and BL2106 are on the Right
Platform 13 (281m)
Platform 15 (277m)
In/Out Road
Catch Point
Note: #3 Reads: Next Signal BL2108

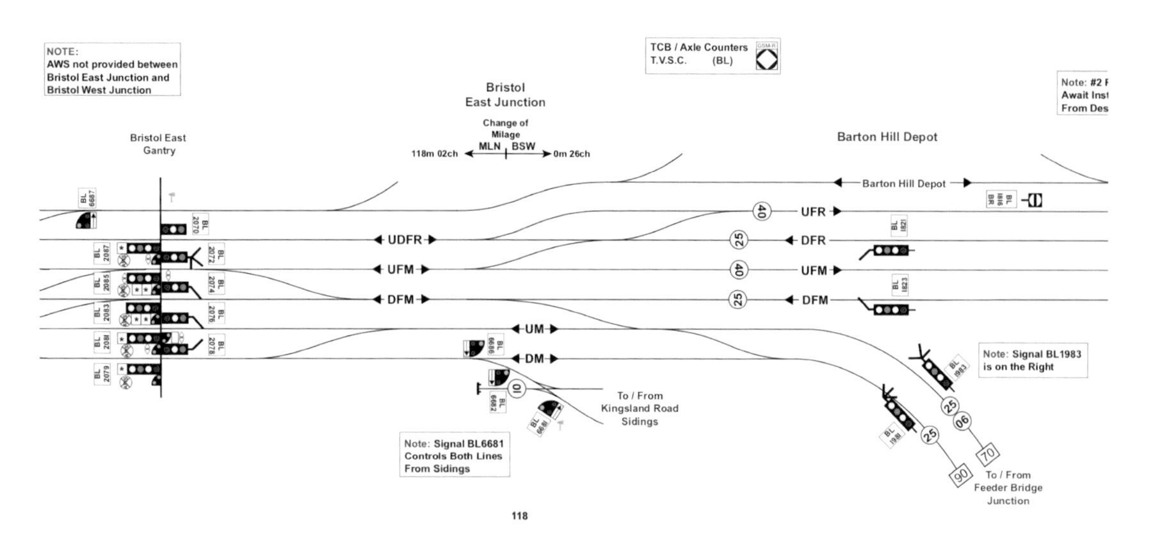

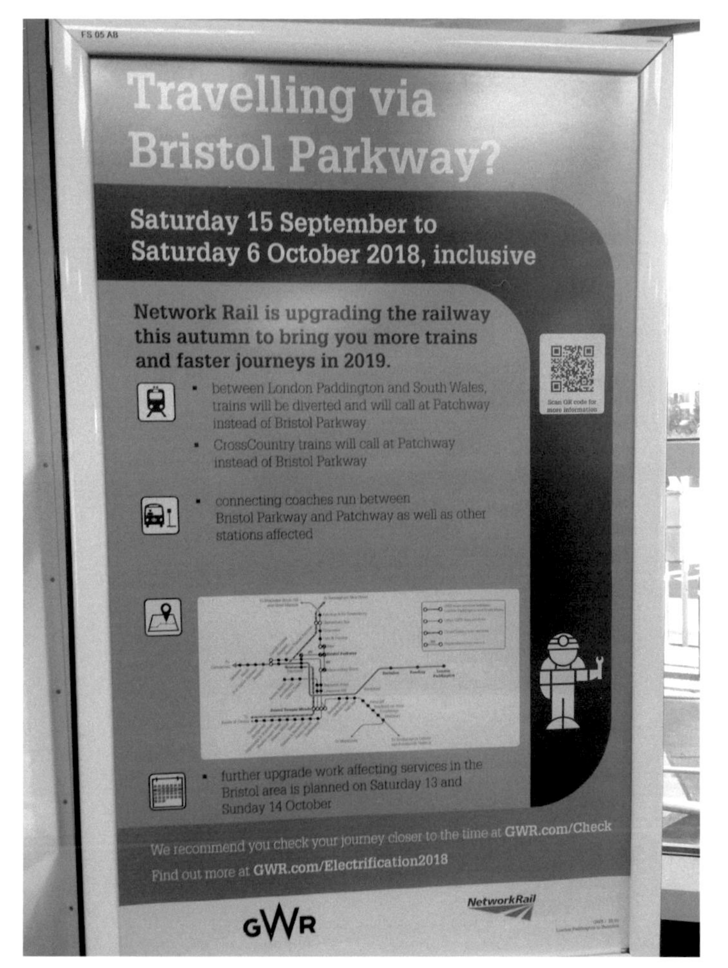

BRISTOL TEMPLE MEADS The works across the region have driven a conscious effort between Network Rail and GWR to advise passenger of forthcoming works and the outcomes in terms of benefits. This board is doing just that at Bristol, before the Easter resignalling.

BRISTOL WEST JUNCTION
Bristol resignalling works in 1969 and 1970 used a steam crane, as in the first view looking towards the station. Fifty years later at Easter 2018 road-railer machines are engaged in the same activity in the same location.

Right: **YATTON** On a lovely spring evening a GWR Bristol-Weston service calls at Yatton. The author had arrived at the village to give a talk to a local railway society on the upgrade works. These reliable DMUs were gauge cleared by Network Rail to use this line by October 2017, allowing longer trains to replace the two-car Class 150 DMUs. In 1970 Yatton had 19 trains each way a day; by 2018 that had increased to 43 each way daily. Passenger growth on the Bristol-Weston line began in the 1990s when the MoD located to Filton Abbey Wood (a new station opened in 1996), and has not abated since, not just to Abbey Wood but also to Bristol, Cardiff and Bristol Parkway.

Centre: **YATTON** On 12 June 1969 a Weston-super-Mare to Paddington train draws into Yatton station hauled by a Class 47 locomotive, captured by the author's father John. Immediately in front of the locomotive is the connection with the former Clevedon branch, closed in 1966. Also noticeable is Yatton signal box, which closed in January 1972; signalling was then controlled by the then new Bristol Panel Box, now itself in its last throes in 2018.

Right: **YATTON** Looking towards Weston-super-Mare from almost the same position, a 10-car IEP train heads from Paddington to Weston on Sunday 2 September 2018. The former Cheddar Valley line bay platforms on the left are now a car park, established in the early 1980s. October 2017 provided quite a revolution on the Bristol-Weston line, with both Class 165 DMUs and IEP trains starting service.

WESTON-SUPER-MARE A GWR Class 165 unit arrives at the station forming a service from Great Malvern, before working its next service to Weymouth. These GWR units started operation on the Bristol-Taunton line in October 2017 after Network Rail gauging works had taken place; the units are longer and wider than the Class 143 and 150 units they displaced on local services, and usefully have a higher seating capacity to deal with the Bristol area rail traffic. GWR of course had a driver training programme to support the cascade of these trains The other Network Rail transformation work evident in this picture is the sign for GSM-R, the digital communications network between drivers and signallers, which went live in this area in 2013.

WESTON-SUPER-MARE Thirty years earlier, on 22 February 1987, Class 45 diesel locomotives and Mark I coaches formed local trains between Bristol and Taunton; in contrast to the Class 165 units, they were bereft of disabled access and spacious toilets.

COWLEY BRIDGE JUNCTION After the floods here just north of Exeter in the previous five years, work has taken place at multiple locations on the Bristol-Exeter route to generate further flood resilience, Cowley Bridge culvert being a good example. Here the new culvert (or underbridge to the lay person) is seen from a drone to good effect as Network Rail-managed works undertaken by AMCO are conducted during a blockade in June 2018. The works were notable for the high volume of activity in a short space of time (76 hours), encompassing track and embankment removal, the installation of 24 concrete sections and a bridge structure, and track replaced and reballasted ready for the start of services on Friday 16 June 2018.

COWLEY BRIDGE JUNCTION In this view looking towards Taunton, the culvert works are in their final hours on Thursday 15 June. The rawness of the new construction, part of a package of South West Rail Resilience works, is evident; in this case they were aimed at avoiding a repeat of flooding events here since 2010.

Above: **COWLEY BRIDGE JUNCTION** The first train over the new structure was the 05.00 freight from Exeter Riverside Yard, ultimately bound for The Potteries loaded with china clay. Bang on time the DB Cargo Class 66 loco gets its precious load of 'white gold' under way. By this time most of the men and women in Network Rail and AMCO had taken to their beds in the knowledge that the works were complete and the railway reopened on time with a job well done.

Left: **COWLEY BRIDGE JUNCTION** Impetus for the flood mitigation upgrade works was scenes that made national television in December 2012, and there have been subsequent events, when just south of the new culvert site the junction of the main Bristol-Exeter line and the Barnstaple line flooded.

COWLEY BRIDGE JUNCTION Another key renewal scheme that took place during 2016/17 was to overhaul and enhance the Exeter Panel signal cabling, installed in 1984. This view is looking towards Cowley Bridge junction.

EGGESFORD The Barnstaple line saw considerable work from 2010 onwards, including many miles of line renewed, together with, at the time of writing, two level crossing upgrades at Salmon Pool (near Crediton) and Eggesford, seen here on 16 March 2016. Platform extensions are also being developed at Eggesford to take longer trains – all very different from the 1980s when railway staff worried that the line might close when the North Devon Link Road and Tiverton Parkway station opened in 1986.

Left: **DAWLISH** 5 February 2014 saw the seawall breached at Dawlish, cutting off Devon and Cornwall. The damage occurred over a 4.2-mile section in multiple locations, which included a 100-metre breach of the wall (and the railway) at Sea View Terrace. Network Rail staff and their contractors were quickly mobilised to start the rebuilding operation in dire conditions. In the meantime GWR and CrossCountry trains initiated a road operation on either side of the breach. In this view staff contemplate the scale of the breach as the down and up lines swing perilously unsupported, while behind them towards Dawlish Warren tonnes of debris were deposited on the lines.

Below: **DAWLISH** In the wake of the seawall breach and damage in multiple locations, the line reopened with much fanfare only six weeks later at the start of April 2014, an amazing effort by the author's Network Rail colleagues and its contractors. The event was marked by a party in Dawlish and a visit by the then Prime Minister David Cameron. In this view, from left to right, Construction Manager Alex Everson is embraced by Projects Regional Director Robbie Burns, with the then Western Route Managing Director Patrick Hallgate and Construction Manager Rob Newton beaming alongside, surrounded by other proud Network Rail colleagues Dai Davies and Lee Haberfield.

Bottom left: **DAWLISH** Seen on 6 February 2014, the damage was not limited to Network Rail infrastructure, as this view demonstrates. Network Rail staff and contractors took this work in hand to restore normality to residents of Sea View Terrace. The battering by the sea continued in the wake of the breach. The men and women in Network Rail who led upgrade and renewal work also led the recovery response in Dawlish; in some cases people worked dynamically and instructions to work were written on Dawlish station platform.

Bottom right: **DAWLISH** A few weeks later the recovery work is under way, led by men and women more used to leading upgrade and renewal works on the Western. Eleven maritime containers were filled with rock to give an element of protection to staff engaged in the rebuilding of the track formation and the seawall as the storm raged. Happily, arising from this event a package of long-term resilience works has been authorised, starting in 2018, following modelling work to determine the right infrastructure solution.

Left: **DAWLISH** In the wake of the 2014 events longer-term work was planned and enacted, and continues currently. In this spring 2015 view looking towards Newton Abbot concrete kerb units are installed to dramatically improve the resilience of the wall.

Below and top right: **DAWLISH** Following development work on long-term solutions for the coastal rail route, initial preventative work commenced as part of an ongoing package to build the resilience of the railway. In May 2018 survey equipment was seen in and around Dawlish as the next phase of the works was developed, and these three photographs show the types of technology used, ranging from survey quad bikes to drones to gather data and inform the next phase of the design works. The views are in Dawlish and on the route south of the station. From the survey work Network Rail engineers and project managers work with the supply chain to develop and single-option the best solutions to protect this iconic piece of railway.

ROYAL ALBERT BRIDGE On Saturday 29 September 2018 Martin Duff captured power cars Nos 43025/43018 crossing the bridge into Saltash with 1C77, the down 'Cornish Riviera', 10.03 Paddington to Penzance. Over a four-year period, 2011 to 2015, the bridge was painstakingly refurbished, keeping the railway open at all times. Removal of ugly access steps revealed once more the lettering that immortalises the brilliant engineer, Mr Brunel.

BODMIN PARKWAY South of Liskeard the signalling block sections vary in length, which makes the repeat pattern of timetabling difficult. Mechanical signalling still exists on the Cornish main line, and British Rail rationalisation schemes left long block sections, which determine line capability. Works therefore took place during 2017/18 between Liskeard and Lostwithiel to provide infill signalling. Here a signalling installation is taking place at Bodmin Parkway, bereft of a signal box since the branch to Boscarne Junction and Wenford Bridge closed after clay trains ceased in 1983. Additionally on the Cornish main line level crossing upgrade works have been undertaken. The effects of these works combine to give increased line capability, allowing GWR to enhance its passenger train frequency south of Plymouth. New signalling in the Bodmin area is controlled from the signal box at Lostwithiel.

SCORRIER South of Truro the Cornish main line passes through an area rich in former tin mine workings. Beyond the ongoing signalling works in the county other transformation work has occurred, including a high spend on long-term measures to protect the railway beside those further up the coast around Dawlish. In March 2018, to address an issue of long-term concern, a mine-capping scheme took place at Scorrier, with evidence of the area's mining history behind the worksite. In this view track is being removed ready to start long-term mitigation measures. The area has many old mine workings and these have been constantly monitored with an eye to keeping the railway safe and avoiding the need to impose speed restrictions. The works at Scorrier were executed by Balfour Beatty in severe weather when a bout of March snow made the work especially challenging.

SCORRIER Thirty-six hours after the possession started in March 2018, final earth removal was completed ready to place concrete segments over the mine workings, lifted in by crane. The workings had been pumped full of polymer grout during many previous weekends. Work continued round the clock to minimise the amount of time the Cornish main line remained closed.

SCORRIER Looking towards Truro, the work is complete, with new track laid over the concrete sections, welded up and ballasted, and ready on time for the first train four days after the work started. The Network Rail Construction Manager captures the scene as the final track work is completed.

PENZANCE and TORQUAY Network Rail work to gauge-clear the whole of the former British Rail Western Region (in the Wales and Western Network Rail routes) has already been mentioned. This work might involve interpreting gauging data by an engineer, and on that basis issuing an authority to run for new trains, or before that can be done it might require physical works such as track slews and cutting back station canopies or platform edges. The latter had to be done at multiple locations to clear the new GWR inter-city trains. The first official new train to reach Penzance was on 17 August 2018, as seen in the first picture, while its counterpart had reached Paignton three weeks earlier and is seen en route at Torquay, captured by Martin Duff.

6. Swindon (Wootton Bassett Junction) to Cardiff

This two-track railway has seen huge changes since 2010. Before electrification could be completed, the route was resignalled, with the traditional Panel Signal Boxes at Swindon, Bristol, Newport and Cardiff ceasing to control the line; phased works since 2010 transferred control to the Railway Operating Centres at Didcot and Cardiff. This work has also seen new track layouts, notably at Cardiff with a new Platform 8.

Multiple overbridges were rebuilt along the corridor to enable electrification, which started in earnest in 2015. By September 2018 electrification works were complete to Bristol Parkway from Swindon, with final efforts then focused on reaching Cardiff.

Additional major works included:

- New depot connections at Stoke Gifford to the IE (Inter-city Express) train depot
- A new track and signalling layout at

BRINKWORTH West of Wootton Bassett Junction, this location was a challenge to strengthen the embankments before the new IEP trains started. In this view a down HST passes the site, destined for South Wales. The works ran for a year and saw excavation of the long embankment and insertion of concrete 'L' units along the base to provide a long-term solution to its stability. Network Rail Construction Manager Mark Swan walks up to the work area to check progress on 25 October 2017. the same year saw high-intensity electrification works, following multiple bridge rebuilds on this route.

Bristol Parkway with an additional fourth platform face and extended platforms, together with the creation of a new third running line west of the station to allow parallel down departures to Bristol and South Wales respectively
- Track lowering in Patchway Tunnels (2015 and 2018) to enable electrification
- A flood mitigation scheme at Chipping Sudbury
- Track lowering at Cardiff on the four-track section under Windsor bridge to enable electrification

BRINKWORTH This view taken on the same day shows an 'out of the box' GWR IEP train, which had been introduced into passenger service the week before. The scale of the concrete units is apparent. The 27 September 2017 blockade saw 33 miles of OLE equipment.

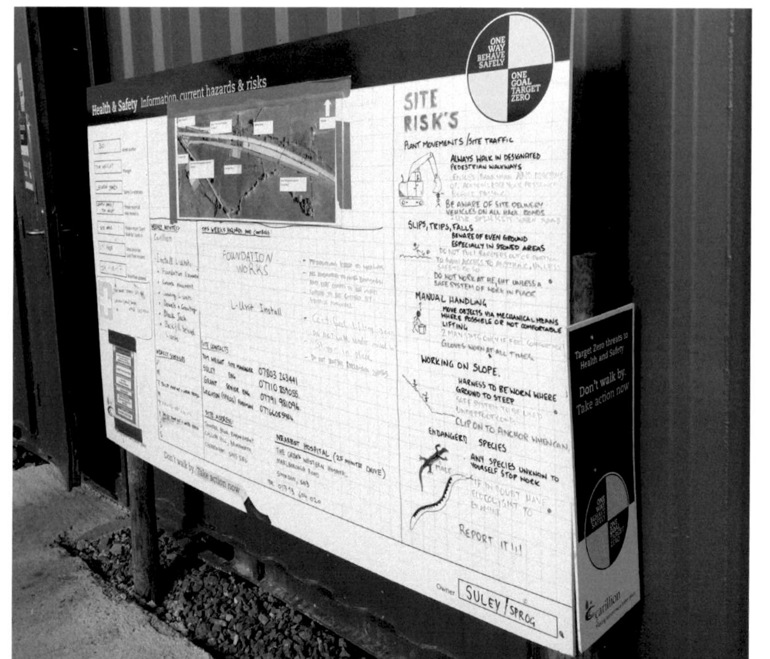

BRINKWORTH The safety noticeboard at this construction site is quite typical. The works were undertaken by Carillion, a company that sadly collapsed in 2018. Regarding the approach to safety, Mark Carne, the former Network Rail Chief Executive (2014-18), was instrumental in driving a strong safety culture at Network Rail such as this, and the concept of 'everyone home safe every day'. No accidents or injuries occurred at this site during its occupation.

BRINKWORTH A little further west, these November 2014 photographs show a new bridge upper structure built on existing abutments. Because the bridge's removal bisected the village, a temporary pedestrian footbridge was built, from which the photos were taken as the author cycled home from work. Because of the effect on local people, these works and other similar upgrade works involved community engagement events and a children's painting competition – with the artwork displayed on the bridge. The works were undertaken here largely while the railway remained open to traffic.

WINTERBOURNE is located west of Westerleigh. The route between Wootton Bassett Junction and Bristol Parkway, passing through Hullavington, saw intense electrification works over the period 2017-18, after the Thames Valley section had been electrified. A major possession on the route in September 2017 saw 33 miles of overhead wires erected in three weeks, and routine night and weekend works continued thereafter. In this view on 15 September 2018 the final works are being undertaken with the installation of the new overhead wiring system. This great achievement meant that by 25 September 2018 the section from Wootton Bassett Junction to Bristol Parkway was complete and ready to be powered up with 25,000 volts. This view is looking towards Westerleigh Junction.

BRISTOL PARKWAY This June 2014 view is from the footbridge, built in 2001, with Freightliner Class 66 No 66537 and a sister machine on empty coal wagons in the yard. By 2016 this area was immersed in upgrade work, as successive photos will show. Freightliner's use of the yard was to support the movement of coal traffic from Royal Portbury Dock along the Portishead branch (which reopened in 2001) to English and Welsh power stations. Since the date of this picture a suite of work has taken place in the middle distance, involving large-scale sheet piling on the left-hand side of the railway, to create space for a third running line alongside the existing two lines. Compare this photograph with that on page 114 with all masts and new lines in situ.

BRISTOL PARKWAY On 17 January 2018 a down GWR service crosses a Manchester-bound CrossCountry service. The second view, looking in the opposite direction, shows the extended platforms, which were completed during the Christmas 2017 works. As can be seen a new, fourth, platform face was added, supplemented by a new layout at the west end that came into use in the summer of 2018, allowing multiple southbound departures.

BRISTOL PARKWAY During a June 2018 blockade through Patchway Tunnel the author recorded progress on works around the station: road-railers at rest between pile erection, a local GWR service waiting to depart from under the new masts awaiting their wires, and a CrossCountry 'Voyager' entering the station, providing a fine view that shows the changes under way with masts erected since the Christmas 2017 platform works.

BRISTOL PARKWAY The opening of the new and extended platforms was marked by a ceremony on 13 April 2018 when the Secretary of State for Transport, Chris Grayling, unveiled this plaque.

BRISTOL PARKWAY In these two views taken just west of the station in mid-September 2018, the huge contrast with the 2014 picture is obvious. Since then the area has been resignalled (2016/17) and signal control transferred to Didcot. At the start of 2018 the new track and signal layout around the station was commissioned after works over Christmas that paved the way for the installation of masts and booms around the station area. Much work was achieved during a three-week blockade that started on 15 September 2018 and ran until 5 October; during that time no passenger trains called at Bristol Parkway. The line blockage also continued to Wootton Bassett Junction to allow other electrification works to be completed. During this period Patchway station was used as a calling point for trains, with CrossCountry services to and from the North diverted via Severn Tunnel and Newport (calling point), then heading via Chepstow to Gloucester to rejoin the scheduled route. GWR London-South Wales trains made the same call at Patchway, with a shuttle bus service between Patchway and Bristol Parkway.

PATCHWAY Summer 2018 saw the removal of the old bridge at Patchway station, which was too low for overhead wires – the replacement is in the background. The station was key as a rail hub whenever access was not available at Bristol Parkway. It is 11 June 2018, before the removal took place, and a large blockade has been put in place embodying the Severn and Patchway tunnels.

PATCHWAY A Class 66 loco heads to the track relay section in Patchway Old Tunnel with wagons of fresh ballast. The blockade started in June 2018 the day that the four-day blockade of the Exeter-Taunton line to install new drainage channels ended.

PATCHWAY TUNNEL The track relay in the Old Tunnel was to lower the track to gain sufficient clearance for overhead wires. The equivalent happened in the New Tunnel in September 2015. Extreme care had to be taken during the works in both tunnels so as not to undermine their structural integrity; staff drew on the lessons of the Penmanshiel Tunnel accident in 1979 when a length of tunnel collapsed, killing staff. The Patchway tunnels are two single-bore structures, at different heights. These photographs were taken on 20 June 2018, and the grimy environs of the tunnel in which the men and women worked can be seen, with track removed and a new (lower) drainage formation being installed. Staff in the tunnel had breathing equipment, and an air extraction system was in operation to keep them safe and well. Monitoring took place to ensure that the structural integrity of the tunnel was not affected as the track formation was lowered. After track removal, the scraping out of old ballast, and the lowering of the drainage system, a new track formation was generated with sand and ballast, following which track laying took place. At that point trains of ballast could come into the tunnel.

Above: **PATCHWAY TUNNEL** Running along the up line on 22 June 2018 a Liebherr road-railer enters the tunnel with two small track sections. There is a newly erected mast on the left.

SEVERN TUNNEL At Ableton Lane, at the east end of the Severn Tunnel, engineers break from their work after a pile refusal – when it cannot be driven in further as planned – on 4 June during the 2018 blockade. In this instance the pile, to the left of the road-rail machine, was cut off and a cap added at ground level to maintain stability of the mast, which had to support a boom spanning four lines. The view, looking towards the Severn Tunnel, shows the recently erected masts and small-part steel.

SEVERN TUNNEL Looking in the opposition direction at Ableton Lane towards Pilning station and Patchway Tunnel, the scale of the works on 20 June 2018 during the blockade is evident, with masts erected and small-part steel and insulators attached to them. On the left is a access point, with a crossing where road-railer machines can move on and off the track.

SEVERN TUNNEL Looking from Ableton Lane towards Patchway only a matter of weeks later on 2 July 2018, the wires have all been installed. One of the road-rail machines deployed for that work is seen in the second picture.

Above: **NEWPORT** There have been a huge number of changes to the Newport station area since this photograph was taken by the author on 25 September 1987 of a Llanwern to Port Talbot iron ore train, with two Class 56 locomotives. The station was enhanced with new station buildings in 2008, the area was resignalled in stages from 2009, leading to the closure of Newport Panel Signal Box, and since 2016 electrification work has taken place. As an aside, the author notes that when he was Operations Manager in Wales the signalmen in Newport and Cardiff signal boxes appreciated two Class 56 locos on these trains for their smart acceleration. Before the end of iron and steel making at Llanwern in 2001 they were hauled by Class 59 locomotives.

Below: **NEWPORT** More than 30 years after the previous photograph, on 10 July 2018 No 158831, forming the 16.34 Newport-Chester service, passes Platform 3 with its canopies under restoration after they have been cut back to give sufficient clearance for the OLE, rather than replaced by new canopies. The signals are controlled from Cardiff. Resignalling of Newport started in 2009 with Newport Panel Signal Box progressively closed, as signalling was re-controlled to Cardiff. By the summer of 2018 OLE masts have already been erected on the Severn Tunnel to Cardiff corridor, with Network Rail contractor Balfour Beatty executing the bulk of the works.

NEWPORT The view towards Cardiff on 25 September 1987 shows an unrefurbished Class 37 locomotive on BDA wagons of steel heading for Llanwern steelworks, with a Plasser tamping machine alongside, when it was inconceivable that the railway in South Wales would ever be electrified. The day the author took this picture he had been to Severn Tunnel Junction Traincrew Depot to say goodbye to colleagues before the depot and yard shut a few days later.

NEWPORT At the same location on 21 September 2018 the efforts of the electrification team can be appreciated, with steelwork and small-part steel in place ready to receive the overhead wires. In the distance a GWR Cardiff-Taunton train approaches the station from Cardiff.

NEWPORT On 10 July 2018, in almost the same spot as the photograph of the two Class 56 locomotives on page 122, a GWR inter-city express train heads for Cardiff. The footbridge is in the final throes of its removal, as in a matter of weeks masts and booms will be installed through the station.

NEWPORT These two views show the state of progress at Maindee Junction, just east of Newport station, on 2 May 2018, with mast erection in progress. The first photo is looking towards the station and the second towards Severn Tunnel Junction.

NEWPORT A diverted CrossCountry train (the 09.30 Bristol Temple Meads to Newcastle) has just come to a stand at Platform 4. Here it will reverse and head back as far Severn Tunnel Junction, then travel via Lydney and Gloucester to rejoin its scheduled route. Evident is the progress since the summer with the erection of masts and booms.

CARDIFF Looking towards the station, where the track has been lowered under the Valley Line network overbridge, engineers complete a track relay on 25 May 2015 not directly associated with the Cardiff resignalling but underpinning subsequent works for electrification. The large interlocking concrete blocks were used to protect trains from the works when cranes were in use in this area.

CARDIFF No 70810 belonging to Colas Rail heads through Cardiff Central in torrential rail with a long train of logs from Chirk to Baglan Bay on 21 September 2018. Noticeable is one of the new signalling gantries erected as part of the Cardiff resignalling, which was a key enabler for electrification. It was completed in December 2017, and was already being overlapped by the electrification works. The two jobs were carefully orchestrated so as not to clash, with Network Rail's Tony Worgan, lead Planning Manager, coordinating and guiding possession requests from differing teams.

CARDIFF This close-up of DB Cargo No 66185 *DP World London Gateway* was taken from a stationary GWR train. Its train was conveying semi-finished steel products from Port Talbot steelworks for processing at Llanwern steelworks. The picture highlights the work by Network Rail's contractor, Alan Griffiths, in cutting back the station canopies to give the clearances necessary for electrification. Work such as this was not readily apparent to the travelling public, but a key enabler.

Introduction to The Subscribers' Limited Edition

by Neil Thompson BSC FRICS

Regional Director Infrastructure Projects, Wales Western and Crossrail

In 2015 I undertook a peer review of the Greater West Programme, which involved a cost and programme analysis of the projects that at that time had a number of challenges to overcome. Despite those dark days, I was immediately struck by the commitment of the people working directly on the programme, and that of others working within the route organisation to provide much-needed support, particularly given the level of complexity to contend with in the execution of the works. The other area that struck me was the strong relationships in existence with the client team under Mark Langman's authentic leadership, which were often challenging but understandable, particularly given that it is not easy to maintain an operational railway when there is a major complex programme of works being delivered.

Following Easter 2017 I took up the post of Regional Director Infrastructure Projects, which encompassed the Greater West and Crossrail programmes within the Western Region with an annual spend of circa £1.5 billion. At that calendar year end we had committed to electrify the railway from Hayes & Harlington to Maidenhead, then later in the year Maidenhead to Didcot. I am pleased to say that both were achieved on programme, bringing immediate passenger benefits and allowing new and longer passenger trains to operate.

The complexity of the works involved to transform the region's railway has seen every discipline of construction engineering involved, ranging from signalling, civil engineering, telecommunications and architecture to track, and overarching all of this has been the design and installation of a new overhead electrical line system delivered by a high-output operation specifically developed for the programme. In my experience of construction and railways going back 35 years I have not witnessed a programme with this level of complexity.

Major programmes of work only get delivered with great people with the right experience, but more importantly with the right behaviours. It is difficult to acknowledge everybody involved in the programme, but I would like to give a special mention to my colleagues within the Western team who have inspired and led from the front, in particular: Simon Maple, David Buisson, Mike Gallop, Jane Austin, Tim Leighton, Chris Fuoco, Nick Millington, Graeme Tandy, Stephen Jenkins, Jon Cunningham, Jonathan Davies, Ben Wheeldon, Dan Tipper, Simon Gardner and Dave Corkett.

Additionally, our suppliers have played a pivotal role in the delivery of the works, much of which Paul has captured in his book, which hopefully showcases their activities. The roll of honour goes to the many people who have played such a crucial part, many of whom appear in these pages.

Finally, I would like to acknowledge Paul for his passion for railways and the time and effort he has put into the publication of this book.

7. The Oxford area

Above and opposite page: **OXFORD** The summer of 2016 saw large-scale works at Oxford, as the track and signal layout was progressively reconfigured ready for its final form in the summer of 2018; a number of other works were also undertaken, including a large flood alleviation scheme to offset flooding that had occurred a number of times in the previous ten years, closing the railway. Early September 2016 saw the deployment of Network Rail's own Kirow crane; until the arrival of the machine, which had been ordered in 2014, Network Rail had hired in Kirow cranes from its supply chain. However, forward planning in 2014 had highlighted the fact that that the Christmas works of 2016 (on the Western Region alone) would exhaust the number of available Kirow cranes, leading Network Rail to order its own. It was first deployed at Oxford after arriving from the construction facility at Leipzig in Germany. The manufacturer found a build slot for it between a batch of cranes being constructed for Chinese Railways. These photographs show the pristine machine working at the west end of Oxford station, laying the new track layout.

MULTI TASKER
66095

OXFORD In April 1981 track renewals were undertaken by British Rail, and it is worth considering the difference in approach between then and now, from a technology and safety perspective. Aside from a common location, another common link is that two members of Network Rail staff on the 2018 rebuild had also worked on this track relay in 1981. This picture shows the Banbury end of the station looking towards Reading, with a BR traxcavator paused; these machines came to the relaying sites on elderly 'Lowmac' wagons, the predecessor of today's road-rail machines that simply drive to the site in rail mode.

OXFORD This second view from April 1981 shows staff engaged in ballast unloading from either 'Sealion' or 'Seacow' bogie ballast wagons – almost risible is the fact that the men are simply wearing office clothes, including everyday footwear rather than steel-soled and steel-toecapped boots, which is now the mandated norm. They are all compliant and wearing orange vests, but all very different from the works in 2016 with the Kirow.

OXFORD Within the station is a three-car DMU with a rake of 'Mermaid' side-tipping ballast wagons standing on the through lines as the dozer undertakes a pass to scrape out the track formation in April 1981.

OXFORD The new platforms for the new Chiltern Railways service to London opened in December 2016, and in this view taken that month showing a Chiltern Class 168 unit fit-out works are still taking place, and continued through to final completion of the works in the summer of 2018. The works were undertaken simultaneously with the upgrade of the Oxford-Bicester line, the completion of which allowed a new direct Oxford to London Marylebone service, thereby making it possible to leave Oxford for London in trains travelling in opposite directions.

OXFORD On the same day, looking towards Banbury, the new station canopy works are evident, having been planned in such a way that train services could largely operate normally. A GWR 'Turbo' unit has arrived at Oxford on a local service from London and waits to enter Oxford Carriage Sidings.

OXFORD This view from the cab of a train at Hinksey, destined for Oxford on 7 July 2018, was taken during the resignalling and remodelling of Oxford that had taken place. A Paddington-bound service, which had started from Oxford, passes in the opposite direction. The area that the HST train is passing was the subject of a large blockade in 2016, when a new culvert was installed under the line as a flood mitigation measure after events of the previous ten years when the River Thames flooded the railway.

OXFORD This view looking towards Banbury is a very unusual one. Temporary buffer stops have been installed, allowing one line into the station to reopen after a major relay during the summer of 2018. The work, carried out between Saturday 7 July and Monday 23 July, included track and civil work on sidings, the raising of platforms to reduce stepping distances for passengers, canopy installation and work on Oxford's new accommodation building. During the blockade Oxford signal box was closed and signal control redirected to the Thames Valley Signal Centre at Didcot. The changes allowed for increased line speeds in the area and better regulation of passenger and freight trains through the station. New power supplies for signals were installed to provide a more reliable signalling system. Teams worked round the clock, with more than 150 staff on site each day, delivering a total of 90,000 hours to complete the work ahead of schedule.

OXFORD On 11 July 2018 staff are hard at work in the heat of the day undertaking the relaying of the lines through the station. In this scene looking towards Banbury a rake of wagons (TOPs-coded KFA) stand loaded with new concrete sleepers while a traxcavator unloads them with a spreader bar, which aids their spacing when laid on the newly ballasted formation. It is worth contrasting this photo with the image taken in April 1981 with the 'Mermaid' wagons standing in the same place.

OXFORD At the start of the blockade in July 2018 the Kirow 250 crane starts lifting track sections and loads them onto 'Salmon' bogie flat wagons at the north end of the station. Air-braked box wagons are used to remove loose sleepers and spoil.

OXFORD At the north end of the station on 11 July 2018 two Volker Rail Kirow cranes (250 Class machines) undertake a tandem lift of new trackwork allied to the installation of the new layout.

OXFORD Seen from the footbridge is a terminating CrossCountry service, with the temporary buffer stop just ahead of the train. Beyond it staff are engaged in finishing the newly laid track.

OXFORD Looking towards Didcot, a High Speed Train enters the station from London. At this time – midway through the July 2018 blockade – one line was reopened to passenger traffic to minimise the amount of time passengers spent on rail replacement buses. As for container freight traffic during the blockade, this was diverted via Reading, Slough and onto the West Coast Main Line, capitalising on the gauge enhancement work completed at the start of 2015 on that route through Slough.

Above: **OXFORD** The Kirow crane is at work at the east end of the station layout on 14 July 2018 lifting new pointwork into place, viewed from the official drone tracking the works.

Left: **OXFORD** At the Banbury end of the station layout on the same day a Class 70 locomotive draws toward Banbury as two Volker rail cranes (both Kirow Class 250s) rest between tandem lift duties.

OXFORD Looking towards Banbury, tandem track lifts are taking place to secure the track into its final correct alignment.

OXFORD This is the Thames Valley Signalling Centre at the new Oxford station on 23 July 2018, with a contented-looking signaller. As a reminder of the old location for any visitors to the signalling centre, a BR Western Region totem sign for Oxford and an old Oxford panel signal post identification plate are on display.

OXFORD This view of the north end of the station from an officially deployed drone was taken on 23 July 2018, with a splendid view of the new layout demonstrating the enhanced capability of the track and signalling now provided to rail users. An interesting dimension is that, following the completion of upgrade works on the Oxford-Bicester line, linked with Network Rail's works at Oxford, there is now a half-hourly Oxford to London Marylebone service, which started in 2017. The new route was used at Christmas of that year for diverted GWR trains travelling from Bristol/South Wales to London owing to the major Crossrail West finishing works on the Slough-Paddington corridor.

OXFORD A slightly different view of the station in the summer of 2018 obtained by the official drone.

8. Reading to Newbury

Before the 2010 upgrade work, the Reading-Newbury line had seen a steady existence with a mix of long-distance high-speed services and a local and semi-fast service on the Bedwyn-Newbury-Reading corridor. The service offering on the route improved in the 1990s when Network SouthEast (Thames and Chiltern) introduced 'Turbo' DMUs and increased service frequencies. Throughout that era the main line was controlled by Reading Panel Signal Box. Then the Christmas 2010 blockade at Reading changed the configuration and saw signalling control pass to the Thames Valley Signalling Centre. Electrification works started in 2014 with the High-Output Machine undertaking work in cyclical possessions – with favourable ground conditions for mast erection (unlike the Reading-Didcot corridor, which proved a challenge).

To maximise the efficiency of the works undertaken and to provide a safe working environment, the 2018 blockades were taken with the support of GWR and DB Cargo, the primary users of the route. This also required closing the level crossings at Thatcham and Midgham overnight during the following closures:

00.45 Monday 4 June to 04.55 Friday 8 June
00.45 Monday 9 July to 04.55 Friday 13 July
00.45 Monday 16 July to Monday 6 August
00.45 Tuesday 28 August to Friday 31 August
00.45 Monday 8 October to 04:55 Friday 12 October

The blockades had high customer impact but did allow significant progress to be made rather than limited windows between trains, or after the last passenger train and before the first train the next morning (less than 6 hours).

READING At the extreme end of the Reading triangle on 27 December 2013 the Kirow crane positions pointwork for the new layout, which was commissioned at Easter 2015.

READING This view from the Network Rail inspection saloon *Caroline* on 14 September 2014, captured by Network Rail Electrification Manager Matt Swancott, shows early mast erection just on the Reading side of Reading West station. Also in view is the new pointwork, centre right, for the new West-East line (installed at Christmas 2013), which now runs within the long-existing triangle formation.

THEALE is the first station out of the Reading suburbs, and the OLE was significantly complete in this picture taken on 13 May 2018 looking towards Reading. The Class 165 unit is standing at the third platform that Network Rail provided in December 2010 as mitigation for passengers when the large Christmas blockade of Reading took place. It is a modular structure and allows step-free access to the coach and car park; in this scene a coach waits for passengers to transfer. The third platform has become a legacy benefit of work mitigations.

SOUTH OF THEALE This looks more akin to Tuscany than West Berkshire countryside! During 2018 the overhead electric power lines along the 40 miles of railway between Reading and Newbury were erected, the work captured to good effect in this photograph. The powerlines were attached to small-part steel-mounted off-masts every 40 to 70 metres along the railway. This photograph was taken on 10 July during the blockade – the reader may recognise that this was the same period as a blockade at Oxford.

THATCHAM station is seen looking towards Reading on 13 May 2018, before the overhead lines had been erected but following mast and boom erection. Each overhead line (a wire run) is 1,400 metres long and needs just over 3½ hours to run out on a straightforward piece of railway. In this photograph both lines are closed to rail traffic as staff prepare for the next phase of the works.

UFTON NERVET There are several level crossings on the Reading-Newbury route, but one in particular had some notoriety and needed be dealt with in the upgrade work. In 2004 a crash occurred here when a member of the public sadly committed suicide by parking his car on the level crossing. This resulted in eight lives lost – the car driver, the train driver and six passengers. A replacement road overbridge was built, from which this photograph was taken; it formally opened on 16 December 2016 and the level crossing was closed. The upgrade work to build the bridge meant relocating the memorial garden established after the events of 2004.

NEWBURY On 14 September 2014, before the mast and wire erection had reached Newbury, a Class 37 locomotive and inspection saloon *Caroline* are seen in the bay platform at Newbury station during an inspection trip in which project engineers and managers reviewed the work and the next steps.

NEWBURY Looking from the track towards the bay platform seen in the previous photograph, on 13 May 2018 preparations are being made to remove the old footbridge and replace it with a modern version. The pleasing Great Western architecture at this station has been retained.

NEWBURY A few weeks later on 4 June, and with canopies repainted, one of the new structures is lifted into place by a road crane during an all-lines-blocked possession. In the distance is another new footbridge – noticeably higher than the old structure seen on 13 May.

NEWBURY The bridge changes captured in the previous photographs paved the way for Amey staff to start the wire runs. Here they are seen on 7 June 2018 in the station area undertaking a wire run working using the High-Output machine, which would travel back to its home base at Swindon after undertaking the work to be fuelled, inspected and reloaded with materials. This view is towards Bedwyn, itself the subject of upgrade work during the same period, when the turnback siding was extended to take new trains, which involved moving a footpath; this work was completed in August 2018.

NEWBURY After the previous photograph was taken staff are now attending to the newly erected wires and will undertake final checks and registration of the new infrastructure. A process then exists for submitting as-built files to the Office of Rail and Road, which will validate the new works and authorise them into use after considering what has been constructed.

9. Bristol area upgrade works: Filton Bank

The 4½-mile section of railway between Lawrence Hill – just north of Bristol Temple Meads – and Filton Abbey Wood was four tracks until the British Rail cutbacks of the 1980s, which saw the section of line reduced to two tracks in 1984 to match the levels of rail traffic then operating. Further reductions in rail traffic came in February 2004 with the cessation of Royal Mail traffic, although this was offset to a degree by a rise in rail passenger traffic, in part caused by the presence of the MoD offices at Filton Abbey. To address this growth, therefore, part of the upgrade of the Bristol area rail network was to reinstate the four-track section of railway and renew the large underbridge at Stapleton Road, the condition of which was stated by British Rail to be one of the causes of the removal of two of the four tracks in 1983.

Service frequency has also much improved since 1984. Then the Cardiff-Portsmouth service was one train every 2 hours, while now it is hourly; Bristol-Severn Beach was one train per hour (in the peak) and now every 30 minutes; and from the North East to the South West was one every 90-120 minutes and is now one every 30 minutes. The 30-minute-frequency cross-Bristol passenger service from Bristol Parkway to Weston-super-Mare simply did not exist in 1984 and the Bristol-Cheltenham-Worcester local service operated only every 2 hours.

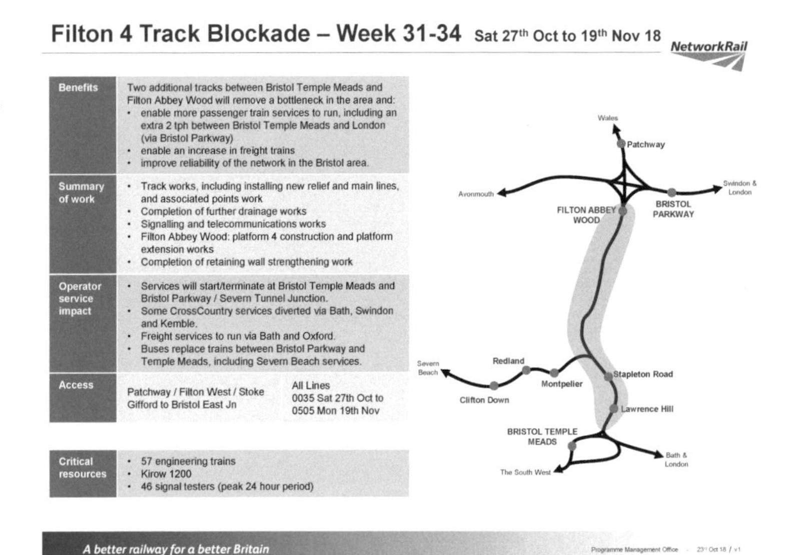

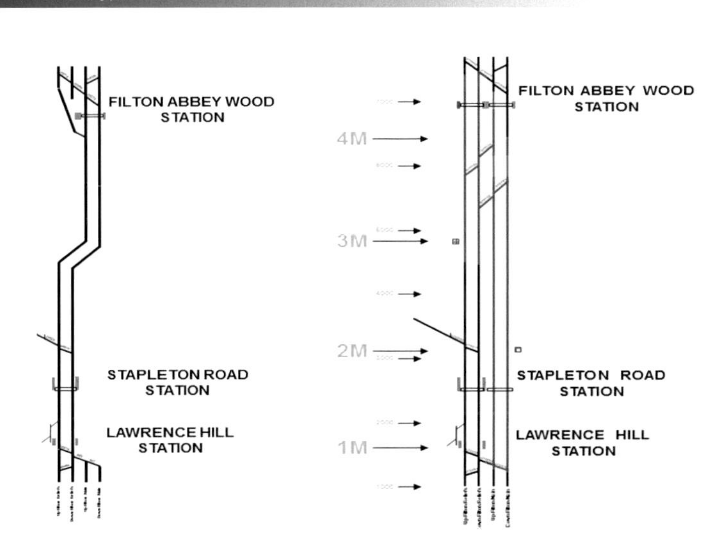

A diagram illustrating the 'before and after' layouts with the reinstatement of the four tracks.

A Network Rail poster giving the public information about the forthcoming works linked to the new footbridge at Stapleton Road.

Above: **FILTON ABBEY WOOD** To set the scene, this is the station on 21 September 2018 as work is completed to provide a fourth platform at the station, the point at which the four-track layout starts.

Below: **FILTON ABBEY WOOD** On the same day, looking north towards Bristol Parkway, a Class 158 DMU leaves the station destined for Bristol Temple Meads as staff work through the pouring rain.

Right: **FILTON ABBEY WOOD** Again looking north towards Bristol Parkway, but a month earlier from the station footbridge, a Class 150 unit passes the track formation works for the new fourth line. The station had opened in 1996 with two platforms, a third being added 10 years later to meet growth.

Below: **FILTON ABBEY WOOD** Looking south towards Horfield and Stapleton Road station, the progress by the end of the summer of 2018 is evident. Before track formation and drainage works took place, the cutting sides were secured and strengthened, including the use of gabions (rock-filled baskets). Track installation has since taken place and a November 2018 blockade saw the lines connected to the existing infrastructure.

Left: **HORFIELD** South of Filton Abbey Wood station new pointwork was installed, and this May 2018 scene, looking north, shows the Kirow crane engaged in laying out the new track; these are long switches that will allow trains to pass through them at high speed.

Right: **HORFIELD** South of the previous photograph – the distant brick bridge being the linking feature – an event occurred on 4 July 2018 to mark the progress with the works. On the left Mark Langman, Network Rail's Western Route Managing Director, holds a banner together with some of the project team, flanked on the right by Andy Cooper, Managing Director of CrossCountry Trains, one of the beneficiaries of the works besides GWR and freight operators.

ASHLEY DOWN At the site of the former Ashley Hill station, progress with the four-tracking is clearly visible, with work continuing on clipping up and ballasting the newly laid track following embankment strengthening works. A GWR Class 158 unit heads down Filton Bank towards Narroways Hill Junction on 21 September 2018.

Right: **NARROWAYS HILL JUNCTION** Looking north towards Ashley Down, a Newcastle to Bristol CrossCountry train, which has run via Gloucester, Lydney and Newport because of the three-week Bristol Parkway blockade, drops down Filton Bank. It had stood at the junction signal for 5 minutes waiting for a GWR train to come off the Severn Beach branch – this problem would be alleviated with the opening of the four-track section at the end of 2018.

Below: **NARROWAYS HILL JUNCTION** Looking towards Stapleton Road station, a GWR Class 165 'Turbo' unit comes off the Severn Beach branch, the cause of the down CrossCountry HST having to wait by the former Ashley Hill station for a clear route. Evident to the left of the unit is the new pair of lines; to the left of them was formerly the route to Mangotsfield, closed in 1970.

STAPLETON ROAD On 8 August 2018, looking towards Narroways Hill Junction, a GWR Class 165 DMU draws to a halt forming a service from Bristol Parkway as staff press on with establishing the new track formation. At the far end of the worksite is the new underbridge installed the previous month in a night-time operation.

STAPLETON ROAD The bridge here was one of the primary reasons cited by British Rail when it closed two of the four lines to rail traffic in 1984. It was removed in September 2017, paving the way for the new structure to be installed in July 2018.

STAPLETON ROAD Before installation of the new structure took place, local artist Ian Cryer created an oil painting of the preparatory works. Ian often works real-time onsite with his artwork, and more details of his work can be found at www.iancryer.co.uk.

STAPLETON ROAD 2 July saw the new structure installed overnight using remote multiple-controlled Self-Propelled Modular Transporters (SPMTs), which inched the new bridge beams into place, as captured in this view looking towards Bristol city centre.

STAPLETON ROAD That night it was smiles all round from Network Rail's Jonathan Davies, Area Delivery Director, and David Buisson, Programme Director, responsible for the delivery of the Filton Bank works and the wider Bristol area upgrade works.

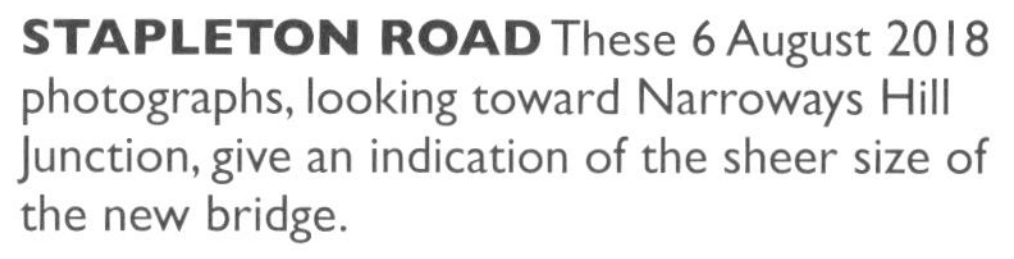

STAPLETON ROAD These 6 August 2018 photographs, looking toward Narroways Hill Junction, give an indication of the sheer size of the new bridge.

STAPLETON ROAD On 21 September 2018, looking towards Narroways Hill Junction, a GWR Class 166 DMU draws to a halt forming a service from Bristol Parkway. Of note is the significant progress since the August picture, as staff have started laying track over the new bridge. Out of site are further supplies of concrete sleepers. Close at hand were signs highlighting changes to access around the station.

STAPLETON ROAD South of the station on 6 August 2018 staff continue the work of refurbishing the bridge over Bannerman Road. Extreme sensitivity had to be shown during this work in a densely populated area that borders the Filton four-track project, with regular stakeholder meetings to keep residents appraised of the work.

STAPLETON ROAD TO LAWRENCE HILL The old Midland main line crossed the GW Main Line here by the bridge seen in the background as track blanketing works progress, following track drainage works and associated earthworks. This view was taken from Easton Road.

LAWRENCE HILL This is the view looking north from the station on 6 August 2018, seen from the old Midland Railway bridge; this used to carry the line that headed to Mangotsfield, which is now a path and cycleway. To the right of the passing Severn Beach line train work progressing on blanketing the track formation ready for track laying to occur, which had happened by the following month. The background bridge carrying Easton Road was replaced at Christmas 2015; the challenges facing staff were somewhat unusual over that period as they were threatened by a man with a handgun.

10. The Golden Valley line

During the period under review the Swindon to Standish line was doubled, the work completed in 2015. This is covered in detail in Silver Link's sister publication *The Golden Valley Line Past & Present* by John Stretton and Tim Maddocks.

Below and right: **STONEHOUSE and KEMBLE** Aside from the redoubling, platform extensions were carried out during 2017 and 2018 at Kemble and Stonehouse; these photographs show work taking place at Stonehouse on Christmas Day 2017 and on 9 September 2018, the day that the works were formally completed.

Left: **STONEHOUSE** January 2018 saw the removal of the footbridge to enable platform extension works to continue; the bridge was reinstated in the summer of 2018. The platform was constructed with polystyrene blocks, then faced with blockwork and topped off with conventional platform coping slabs. The polystyrene solution makes for swift installation and can therefore reduce costs over conventional brick and concrete construction.

11. Westerleigh to Worcester and Barnt Green

The Bristol to Birmingham route has seen several upgrade schemes since 2010, albeit not on a scale of those undertaken on the Bristol to London line. A low-key but important scheme was undertaken in 2017/18 to raise the line speed on the Barnt Green to Westerleigh Junction route, with work on the track and drainage. This work concluded in the autumn of 2018 and will benefit train journeys from 2019 onwards.

At Cheltenham Spa in readiness for new trains, station platform extensions were carried out in time for the summer of 2018. This, aligned with line speed improvements, will really improve the service offering on the route.

WORCESTER In 2016/17 the Worcester area saw extensive specialist work to overhaul and ensure the continued safe operation of mechanical signalling. This is very specialist work, with only a few individuals who are able to re-cut locking bars.

HENWICK In 2017 a new turnback siding was completed at Henwick, west of Worcester Foregate Street. In the 2019 timetable this will allow trains from either Birmingham or London to call Foregate Street, then draw forward into the turnback siding and reverse.

10. The Westbury area

WESTBURY in April 1974 was very different from the Westbury of today. Ten years before the resignalling of 1984, 'Merchant Navy' Class locomotive No 35028 *Clan Line* has arrived on a special train, as a Class 47 diesel locomotive waits to leave on a vacuum-braked freight train. The area was to see further changes after this date, with air-braked aggregates trains and the arrival of the privately owned Class 59 locomotives in 1986.

WESTBURY Since 1974 Westbury has remained an important rail hub. It was resignalled by British Rail Western Region in 1984, eradicating the signal box seen in the previous picture and other boxes in the area. As this photograph by the author illustrates, it remains an important centre as a Class 60 loco shunts long welded rail in preparation for Christmas 2016 works along the Thames Valley for the introduction of Crossrail. The tail end of the train behind the Class 47 in the 1974 shot is where the Class 60 is standing. Ballast is stockpiled here and both the up and down yards are key for the stabling of logistics trains. Westbury is also an important location for GWR, with a train stabling and servicing facility and train crew depot.

MELKSHAM While the rest of the country watched the England game on Saturday 7 July 2018, this train was heading to the Filton Bank four-tracking works, which saw a weekend-long all-lines blockade. The Class 66-hauled train of sand, ballast and concrete sleepers passes through a set of works just completed, that of the platform extension at Melksham. Since the station had reopened in April 1985 it had suffered from a short platform, which was extended at the Thingley Junction end to accommodate three-car Class 158 and 16x DMUs. The author's bicycle rests against the AMCO poster, a company proud of the work it undertook for Network Rail.

MELKSHAM On 27 September the 17.36 Swindon to Westbury three-car DMU calls at the fully completed station platform extension.

13. Crossrail East

Aside from works on the Paddington to Maidenhead section, Network Rail was funded to undertake works on the Great Eastern main line out as far as Shenfield and on the North Kent Line, taking in Abbey Wood. These were significant works in their own right and ran concurrent with the works on the Great Western Main Line. They took place over several years, being completed in 2018, and could fill a book in their own right.

Right: **SHENFIELD** 28 December 2016 saw a large-scale blockade, with rewiring and track relaying taking place at Shenfield in the same vein as works on the Great Western Main Line.

Below: **ABBEY WOOD** As well as the work on the GE main line to support the introduction of Crossrail trains, extensive works occurred on the North Kent Line, as witnessed here at Abbey Wood on 30 December 2015; at this location major track and station works took place over several years. Seen here is formation concreting.

SHENFIELD Finally, something staff working on the Crossrail East works all wanted to see – Crossrail Class 345 nine-car EMUs operating..

14. Heathrow Western Rail Access

While the work of the past eight years has seen practical delivery of works, the planning and development of future projects continues. An exciting proposition is that of a new Western Rail Access to Heathrow, coming off the Great Western Main Line, and design work and consultation work is under way at the time of writing in 2018.

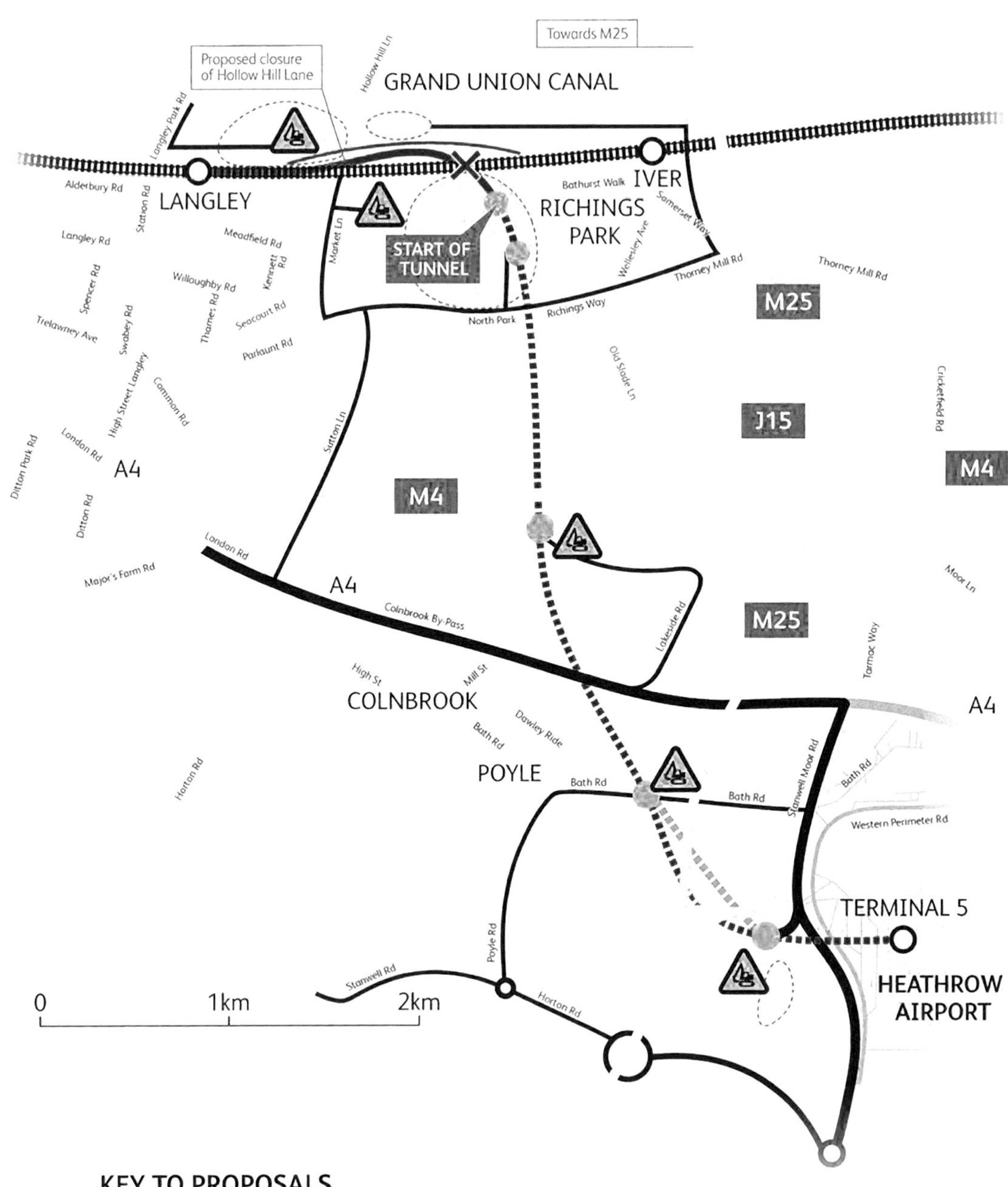
Towards M25
Proposed closure of Hollow Hill Lane
Hollow Hill Ln
GRAND UNION CANAL
Langley Park Rd
LANGLEY
IVER
RICHINGS PARK
Bathurst Walk
Somerset Way
Alderbury Rd
Station Rd
Langley Rd
Meadfield Rd
Market Ln
START OF TUNNEL
Kennett Rd
Wellesley Ave
Thorney Mill Rd
Willoughby Rd
Spencer Rd
Swabey Rd
Thames Rd
Seacourt Rd
North Park
Richings Way
M25
Trelawney Ave
Parlaunt Rd
Old Slade Ln
High Street Langley
Common Rd
Sutton Ln
J15
Crickelfield Rd
London Rd
A4
M4
Ditton Park Rd
Ditton Rd
London Rd
Major's Farm Rd
Moor Ln
A4
Colnbrook By-Pass
Lakeside Rd
M25
Tarmac Way
High St
Mill St
COLNBROOK
A4
Dawley Ride
Bath Rd
POYLE
Horton Rd
Bath Rd
Bath Rd
Stanwell Moor Rd
Bath Rd
Western Perimeter Rd
TERMINAL 5
HEATHROW AIRPORT
Poyle Rd
Stanwell Rd
Horton Rd
0
1km
2km
KEY TO PROPOSALS
RAIL EXTENSION
TUNNEL
NEW LINES ON EMBANKMENT
POTENTIAL CHANGE TO PATH OF TUNNEL
ACCESS ROUTES TO COMPOUNDS
ACCESS BUILDING
MAIN COMPOUNDS
SMALLER SITE COMPOUNDS (Indicative only)
FLOOD STORAGE AREA
NEW RAILWAY INTERSECTION BRIDGE
EXISTING HEATHROW BOUNDARY
EXISTING STATION

Network Rail

A

Lee Ackerman
Christopher Ackerman
Titilayo Adenrele Williams
Mohamed Addan
Jo Addison
Ifepade Adekoya
Jonathan Adkins
Luke Agbenyo
Hannah Ager
Matthew Ager
Steve Ahier
Aaqib Ahmed
Ali Ahmed
Humna Ahmed
Khadra Ahmed
Sammia Ahmad
Shanoor Ahmed
Paul Ainsworth
Dele Ajiboye
Andrew Ajube
Mohammad Akbar
Abdul-Ahad Akbari
Adegboyega Akomolafe
Sandra Akposheri
Olalekan Alatise
Matthew Alderson
Chrissy Alderson
Syed Ali
Yusuf Allali
Elizabeth Allan
Gary Allan
David Allchin
Chloe Allen
Laurence Allen
Mark Allen
Patrick Allen
David Alleyne
Steve Alston
James Alton
Valentina Alupoaei
Obinna Amadi
Hassan Amin
Mohamed Amin
George Amporfro
Sohail Anwary
Aramide Arasanmi
John Archard
Delia Areias
Richard Armand
Ade Armolaran
Aleksandra Arnista
Kwame Arthur
Richard Arthur
Michael Ash
Anita Atas
Ibrahim Atcha
William Atere-Roberts
Paul Atherton
Grace Atherton
Darren Atwood
Jane Austin
Mark Austin
Anand Avvaru
Hassan Ay
Adeel Azam

B

Cameron Badenoch
Aleksandra Badger

ST GERMANS The Cornwall resignalling schemes completed in 2018 gave additional capability to GWR's planned new train service south of Plymouth. Here the team take a break for the camera.

Roll of Honour

Andrew Bailey
Gary Bailey
Martin Bailey
Martin Baker
Susan Baker
Ian Baldwin
Amy Bale
Tim Ball
Mike Bane
Otitokan Bankole
David Bardwell
Kenneth Barma
Sarah Barnett
Ian Barnicoat
Sophie Barrett
Baillo Barry
David Bartlett
George Bartlett
Thomas Bartlett
Davinder Singh Bassan
Craig Bassett
Derinder Basson
Andrew Battersby
Richard Battersby
Geoffrey Bean
Arthur Beard
Robert Beattie
Sarah Jane Beaumont
Edward Beausire
Simon Beevers
Susan Bell
Simone Benedettelli
Emmanuel Ben-Edigbe
Sekoura Benissad
Alex Bennett
Matthew Bennett
Richard Berg
Marta Berryman
Malcolm Best
Divya Beta
Narad Bhandari
Navneet Bhinder
Marc Bickerstaff
Steven Bickler
Wayne Billett
Jemma Birkin
James Bishop
Benjamin Bissett

Jane Austin BEng (Hons) FICE, MICE, CEng

As the Head of Engineering for the region, this has been both fun and technically challenging over the past five years. I am accountable for all aspects of engineering, leading a team of up to 347 engineers at our busiest and ensuring delivery of robust outputs for the major upgrade programme on the Great Western Main Line. The route is 216 miles long and is seeing new signalling, new overhead line systems (Series 1 Overhead Line Equipment) and three new fleets of trains. It is the largest upgrade programme that Network Rail has ever undertaken.

The work saw the introduction of many new technologies on the network, including Series 1 OLE, which is first of type Freur and Frey system. This took into account the existing failures/faults of previous OLE systems, which were designed out as part of the new design. This has also driven the implementation of the dynamic modelling (interface between train pantograph and overhead line) and we have managed the creation of the system on a test track to demonstrate the dynamic performance. The results from the testing required no significant changes to design.

Power and Distribution as part of this OLE system also introduced atomised rational distribution system (RATS), which is cutting-edge technology. No other railway line has this currently. Power enters from the National Grid into the substations and RATS will isolate the overhead line system, work out the location of a fault, discount the fault, then re-energise. This improves availability and reliability of the OLE.

The European Train Control System (ETCS) and Supervisory Control and Data, which is a replacement for legacy train protection systems, has seen deployment on a part of the Great Western Main Line.

With a very short and tight timeframe to deliver, a supervisory control and data acquisition (SCADA) system for the OLE was introduced on the Western Region from 2016. This is an operator interface system that enables monitoring and the issuing of process

commands; the system integrates electrical control into a Rail Operating Centre at Didcot, the location of the Thames Valley Signalling Centre.

All these aspects give a sense of the enormous engineering technical challenges. These challenges have been multiplied by the evolution of new standards and legislation that have needed to be complied with, such as Common Safety Method to ensure that from a systems perspective we understand the true requirements, and hazards are eliminated through design and construction before handover to the operator and maintainer through the life of the project. For the region I have led the introduction of Interoperability, which was introduced to promote a single market in the rail sector.

Working closely with the Department of Transport (DfT) and the Office of Rail Regulator, I successfully agreed the 1st Authorisation Strategy in Network Rail. In addition, there is huge expectation that this new railway will not only be ultra-reliable, but also safer than any of its predecessors.

ROLL OF HONOUR

Christopher Black
Emily Blackwell
Richard Blake
Adam Blakeman
Adrian Boast
Michelle Boland
Anthony Bolton
Francis Bolton
Paul Booth
Allan Bott
Paul Boulter
Geoffrey Bounds
Brahim Bouqourri
James Bowry
Neil Boys
Marilena Bracho
Stephen Bradley
David Brady
Joel Bragg
Tim Brain
Brian Bramley
Zakari Braou
Matthew Brawley
Tony Brennan
Moelwen Brennan Evans
Wayne Bridgen
David Brittain
Nicola Britton
Ander Broadman
Johnpaul Brooker
Ezekiel Brooks
David Brown
Hugh Brown
Ian Brown
Jacquie Brown
Nigel Brown
Robert Brown
Catarina Brunckhorst
Mike Brunt
Stephen Bryden
Robert Buckby
Giuseppe Bufalini
Richard Bugler
David Buisson
Cornelia-Gabriela Bulai
Stuart Burrows
Muberra Bushell
Fiona Bussell
Emma Butchart
Elizabeth Butcher
James Butler
Timothy Butler
Ronan Byrne
Paul Byrne

C

Peter Cabral De Abreu
Frank Cadona
Robert Cahill
Karen Cairns
James Calder
Alex Cameron
Darren Campbell
Graeme Campbell
Wendy Campbell
Jonty Cann
Jacqueline Carroll
Nick Carter
Marcus Cashin
Oscar Castillo
Peter Caulfield
Micheal Cella
Jagdip Chahal
Felix Chamberlain
Gregory Chambers
Jack Chang
Anna Chapman
Ian Chapman
John Charlton
Joshua Cheema
Lee Cheetham
Oi Ki Cheung
Chiansye Chia

HORFIELD In May 2018 a rake of tilting wagons arrives with new pointwork for the junction south of Filton Abbey Wood station, reading for commissioning later in the year.

Roll of honour

Christopher Chidwick
Robert Chik
Mary Chirwa
Panashe Chisasa
Mariette Chishick
Bridgit Choo-Bennett
Hans Chowdhury
David Chubb
Allan Chung
Philip Churchill
Bogdan Ciocoiu
Nicola Clancy
Eliot Clark
Margaret Clark
Samuel Clark
Katherine Clarke
Shaun Cluderay
Gareth Clwyd-Jones
Nicole Coady
Paul Coates
Steve Coe
Benedict Cole
Richard Coleman
Ian Collins
Kevin Collins
Katie Collinson
Alex Conn
Hugh Connell
Ian Constantine
Andrew Cook
Gary Cook
Oliver Cook
Nicholas Cooke
Lorraine Coomber
Nicholas Cooney
Kenna Cope
Peter Corbas
Jonathan Corbishley
Stephen Corcoran
Locksley Cordery
David Corkett
Peter Corneck
Lee Coulson
Andrew Couret-Row
Claire Cowan
Luke Coxhead
Thomas Coxon
Janice Crawford
Katherine Crawley
Denise Creek
June Croft
Duane Cronje
Debra Csapo
Kirk Culley
Jonathan Cunningham
Loren Curry
Stephen Cussons
Terry Cutts

D

Alex Daintree-Blackshaw
Katherine Dalton
Lee Dalton
Abdullahi Wahida Dambam
Jonathan Daniels
Andrew Daubney
Stephen Davidson
Bradley Davies
Jamie Davies
Jonathan Davies
Martyn Davies
Jason Davis
Robin Davis
Thomas Davis
Peter Dearman
Oluwadamini Dele-Oladipupo
Alan Derbie
Sean Dermody
Emmanuel Deschamps
Carol Deveney
Sean Devaney
Sharon Devlin
Kanwal Dhillon
Antonio Di Caprio

EALING BROADWAY On Christmas Eve 2016 travellers attired as Mexicans head off for a day in London, changing onto the Central line as the line ahead is blocked for major works between Acton Yard and Paddington. 'Del Boy', 'Rodney' and 'Grandad' were spotted later that morning travelling to Swansea.

Dave Ditchfield
Andrew Dix
Zoe Dixon-Saunders
Stephen Dodd
David Dolby
David Dolby
Lee Dolby
Michael Dommett
Mary Doody-Jenkins
Sen Jay Dookayka
Sundip Dosanjh
Carole Douglas
John Doyle
Adam Drake-Brockman
Sam Dring
Alan Drummond
Martin Duff
Howard Duffy
Anne Dugdale
Sean Duggan
Orla Dunn
Andrew Dunnett
Andrew Durrant
Michael Durrant
Andrew Dutton
Rupert Dutton
Darren Dykstra
Mike Dyson

E

Toby Eccles
Mike Edmunds
Neil Edmunds
Alex Edwards
Andrew Edwards
Gavin Edwards
Ian Edwards
Stephen Edwards
Steven Edwards
Thomas Edwards
Mark Eldridge
Howard Elliot
Toby Elliot
Deborah Elliott
Lee Elliott
Philip Ellis
John Ellison
Billie Else
Adrian Emerson
Simon Ernest
Dare Esezobor
Carlos Espinosa Portales
Adrian Evans
Alun Evans
Emma Evans
Huw Evans
Hywel Evans
Ian Evans
James Evans
Lee Evans
Wayne Evans
Alex Evason
Louise Evatt
Chioma Ezendiokwele

F

John Fagan
Aimee Fairhurst
Bernard Fanning
Emily Farhall
Simone Farmer
Osmond Farooq
Lee Farrell
Robert Farrell
Jake Faucitt
Roderick Fawcett
Paul Fellows
David Feltham
Patrick Ferguson
Franklin Fernandez
Anne Field
Susan Field
Emma Fielding
Michael Finan
Wayne Fish
Eric Fitzgerald
Jack Flanagan
William Flavelle
Dragos Florean
Sara Fluck
Sinead Foley
Christopher Ford
Terry Fordham
Jaime Fornieles
Kenneth Forshaw
David Forshaw
Shaun Fortes
Thomas Foster

WOOTTON BASSETT JUNCTION On Christmas Day 2015 an undertrack crossing is installed for high-voltage cables to support electrification work. Behind the operative is the rail-served aggregates terminal.

Andrew Foulds
Sean Francis
Kwesi Francois
Mike Franklin
Richard Franklin
Jacob Freckleton
Christine Freeman
Carlie French
Bianca Fucito
Chris Fuoco

G

Darren Gadd
Ravi Kishore Gadepalli
Guy Gahir
Divya Gaikwad
Mike Gallop
Andrew Galt
Russell Gange
Danny Gard
James Gard
Ed Gardiner
Andrew Garner
Simon Gardner
John Gaze
Ayodele Gbede
Michael Gear
Mark Geary
Peter Gentry
Gavin George
Simon George
Niall Gibbons
Jeremy Gibbs
Paul Gibbs
Dave Gilbert
Lee Gilbert
Leon Gilchrist
Rhys Giles
Stephen Giles
Melanie Gilhooly
James Gillanders
Brian Gillespie
James Gilliatt
Nattashar Gittens
Mark Glaysher
Freddie Gleeson
Alexandra Glenn
Agata Gmerek
Finian Gogarty
Duncan Golding
Manuel Gomes da Costa
Tracey Gooden
Paul Gooding
David Goodliff
Christopher Goodwin
Dawn Gotobed
Alan Gough
Wayne Gould
Stephen Gow
Mark Gratland
Lionel Gray
Michael Gray
Andrew Greaves
Stuart Green
Richard Greenwood
Joanne Griffiths
Samuel Griffiths
Peter Grosvenor
Clarisse Grother
Herbert Gruntman
Tanushri Gukhool
Ginka Guncheva
Andrew Gurd

H

Lee Haberfield
Paul Hackett
Michelle Hales
Steve Haley
David Hall
Steve Hall
Patrick Hallgate
Lynne Halman
Keith Halton
Ashley Hamer
Tanya Hampson
Geoff Hancox
Lisa Hannah
Robert Hannon
Victor Hanson
Anthony Harding
David Hardy
Suzanne Hardy
Luke Hare
Matthew Hargreaves
Fergus Harkins
Dominic Harris
Naomi Harris
Deborah Harrow
Steven Hart

MAIDENHEAD In June 2017 Route Managing Director Mark Langman speaks in advance of Prime Minister Theresa May, who will perform the official opening ceremony, watched by staff of the Network Rail Crossrail project.

Roll of Honour

Abigayle Harvey
Philip Harvey
Sam Havill
Jonathan Hayes
Paul Hayes
George Hayllar
Clive Head
Jack Heath
Denise Helmkay
Colin Hemming
Christopher Hemsley
Kerry Hemsley
Scott Henderson
Donna Henry
Mike Henry
Brian Hepworth
Charles Heseltine
Kimberley Hibbert
Emily Hickling
Thomas Hickman
Darren Higgs
Lucie Higgs
Andy Hill
Marcus Hill-Jones
Keith Hindhaugh
Roy Hines
Philip Hingley
Stuart Hitch
John Hoare
Anita Hobson
Alan Hodge
David Hodgson
Gavin Hodson-Walker
Lucy Hogg
Nigel Hollingworth
Peter Holloway
Lucy Homewood
Alastair Hood
Robert Horgan
Amanda Horton
Ali Hossain
Maroof Hossain
Megan Hotson-Moore
Leigh Howard
Rhys Howells
Timothy Howells
Xiaomei Hu
David Hubbuck
Joseph Hudson
Caeo Hughes
David Hughes
Nicky Hughes
Thomas Hughes
Peter Hume
James Hunter
Robert Hustwick
David Hutchens
Steve Hutchinson
Briana Huthwaite
James Hutt

I

Kidd Ian
Alan Iles
John Impey
John Imrie
Javier Inarejos
Uzma Iqbal
Christian Irwin
Pippa Irwin
Eunice Israel
Maria Ivory
Steve Ivory

J

Amy Jackson
Christopher Jackson
Lisa Jackson

OXFORD During the July 2018 blockade to finish the remodelling and resignalling of Oxford, this was the view towards Banbury, showing relaid lines and ongoing station enhancement works.

ROLL OF HONOUR

Matthew Jackson
Matthew Jacobs
Carl James
Christopher James
Matthew James
Steven James
Nigel Jarvis
Nigel Jarvis
Michelle Jassi
William Jeffries
Stephen Jenkins
Alex Jenkins
Ian Jenkinson
Eric Jeyes
Telvinder Jheeta
Indira Jheinga
Nigel Jobbins
Himalee John
Christopher Johnson
Joanne Johnstone
Bryn Jones
Charlotte Jones
David Jones
Gavin Jones
Kieran Jones
Kris Jones
Rhys Jones
Stephen Jones
Gurveesh Joshi
Juhi Joshi
Milind Joshi
Cormac Jupe

K

Abul Kalam
Godfrey Kaliu
Shivdev Kalyan
Kanapathipillai Kanthasamy
Gagandeep Kaur
Suzanne Kay
Fintan Kearns
Stephen Keehn
Duncan Keeling
Alistair Keen
Timothy Keenan
Bryan Keetch
Steve Keighley
Fabrice Kemdjo Wouche
Scott Kennedy
Andrew Kennedy
Mohammed Khalef
Mushtaque Khan
Fathema Khatun-Ahmed
Stuart Kidd
Sianne Kilbane
Paul Kilby
Andrew King
Robin King
Peter Kingwell
Keith Kirwin
Steffan Kitchen
Ruth Kitson-Smith
Rowan Klimaytys
Melanie Knightwood
John Knowd
Yamini Kumar
Michal Kuzdub

L

Rudi Laas
Reinhold Labisch
Daniel Lacey
Simon Laird
Nicholas Lake
Thomas Lamarque
Trevor Lambert-Gorwyn
Troy Lancaster
Anthony Lane

PADDINGTON On 16 August 2018 a useful comparison is presented between Crossrail and GWR EMU trains. While looking different, they have the common characteristic of a high capacity for passengers

ROLL OF HONOUR

Mark Langman
Karolina Langova
Steve Lant
Peter Last
Charles Lateu-Smith
Julie Laverie
Sinead Lawlor
Aidan Lawson
Nathan Lawson
Stuart Lay
Christine Lazarus
Frankie Lazzara
Martin Leach
Jonathan Leadston
Charlotte Lee
Charlotte Lee
Gareth Leese
Stephen Leigh
Tim Leighton
Scott Lerski
Phillippa Lesforis
Mark Lewin
Amy Lewis
Emma Lewis
Lisa Lewis
Philip Lewis
Stephen Lewis
Edward Lewis-Cox
Kelly Lincoln
David Linley
Stephen Lock
Rebecca Lomax
Carlo Lorusso
Sarabjit Lota
Balbindra Lovell
David Lovell
Nicholas Low
Adam Lucas
Natasha Luddington
Matthew Lupton
Emily Luszcz
Rhiannon Lynch

M

John MacDonald
Jessica Mace
Iain Mackenzie
William Mackinnon
Alan MacLean
Stuart Maddock
Jason Maggs
Nicholas Maher
Danny Maile
Vinay Maini
Alastair Mair
Antonella Maizza
Paul Malaney Jnr
Sarbjeet Malhi
Fowad Malik
Fergal Malone
Jason Malschuk
Joanne Mandeville
Andrew Manina
Beverly Manna
Ian Mansfield
John Mansfield
Shayne Manuel
Simon Maple
Catherine Marasigan
Jimmy Marasigan
David March
Hector Marcos
Alex Marsh
Margaret Marsh
Stephen Marsh
Lucy Marshall
Steve Martin
Adrian Martin

READING On 17 June 2014 there was a photo-call with Her Majesty the Queen. The line-up of staff in orange included Bechtel and GWR colleagues who had helped bring the Reading remodelling scheme to completion.

Roll of honour

Christopher Martin
Nicholas Martin
Robert Mashford
Andrew Mason
Simon Masters
Andrea Mathers
Samantha Mathers
Helen Mathewson
Stephen Mathias
Rui Matos
Hayley Matthews
John Matthews
David Maxwell
Graham May
Stephen Mayhead
Mariattee Mayisa
Mihaela Mazilu
Noel McCarville
Daniel McCarville
Oliver McCauley
Michael McCormack
Jonathan McCorriston
John McDermid
James Mcdonald
Peter Mcdonald
Matthew McEwen
Christopher McGarry
Claire McGine
Deborah McGrath
Neil McGuire
Samantha McHugh
Wayne McIntosh
Henry McKenna
Philip McMahon
James McNamara
Stephen McPherson
Paul McQuillan
Janine McShane
James McWhirter
Tim Mead
Michele Mee
James Meredith
Figan Meric
Richard Merrett
Craig Micallef
Sharon Michell
Andrew Midgley
Nick Milington
Lucy Millard
Paul Miller
Ryan Miller
Shane Miller
Scott Millward
Rebecca Milsom
Jamie Mirams
Susan Mitchell
Billy Mogg
Miguel Molina-Ortega
Jason Molyneux
David Moore
Eric Moore
John Moore
Timothy Moore
Dave Moorehouse
Ailsa Moorhead
Dave Moorhouse
Daniel Moran
Eric Morgan
Gerard Morgan
Michael Morgan
Peter Morgan
John Moriarty
Ewen Morrison
Mark Morrison
Elaine Mortiboy-Clarke
Damian Mortimer
Philip Morton
Emma Moss
Lisa Motley
Gilles Moullec
Francois Mouton
Nasifu Mugisha
Richard Mulholland
Kirsten Murison
Dave Murphy
Philip Murphy
Innes Murray

READING On 30 December 2014 final checks are carried out to newly laid and tamped trackwork in this view looking towards the station from the Bristol end of the layout.

Paris Murray
Piotr Muszynski
Nomalizo Mwale

N

Kelvin Nagberi
Suleman Nakhooda
Mlungisi Ncube
Paul Needham
Roy Neve
Paul Nevett
Paul Newman
Keith Newton
Robert Newton
Richard Nice
Hollie Nicholls
Jodie Nicholls
Jonathan Nicholls
Abigail Nichols
Sarah Nicholson
Anna Nicol
Lesley Nidd
Navjeet Nijjar
Anita Niklas
Veerasingam Nimal Anathan
James Noble
Martin Noke
Bradley Nolan
John Nolan
Karl Norman
Nikki Norris
Sarah Norton
Daniel Nsiah-Ababio

O

Joseph O'Brien
Maria O'Brien
Michael O'Connell
Anthony O'Dea
Matthew O'Leary
David O'Mahony
James O'Neill
Prince O'Neill Iqbal
Richard O'Nion
Pat O'Sullivan
Gary Oakes
Jamie Oakey
Rebecca Oaten
Michael Obata
Uchenna Obieme
Atul Odedra
Alexander Odiase
Simon Offley
Michael Ogbechie
Tokunbo Ogunsola
Sheila Okoro
Christopher Okwegwa
Ileana Oncescu
Vera Onuoha
Oluwafemi Oresajo
Daisy Osei
Anuoluwapo Oshisanya
Steve Otoo
Ian Oughton
Ejiro Oweh
David Owen
Justin Owens
Victoria Oyegunle
Purvi Oza
Barish Ozdogru

P

Joanne Paddington
David Paddison
Juan Antonio Padilla
Gareth Pagett
Peter Painter
Kirsten Pal
Michael Palmer
Barnaby Panners
Robert Parkes
Matthew Parkin
John Parmenter
Andrew Parrett-Jung
Brian Parry
Lynne Parry
Sarah Parry
John Parsons
Louise Parton-Ginno
Vijayalaxmi Passmore

WEST EALING At Christmas 2015 staff complete the relay to the reconfigured junction. On the left out of sight is the Plasser on-track machine factory, which is rail-served.

ROLL OF HONOUR

Leonard Passmore
Cliff Patch
Muneer Patel
Victoria Paterson
Colin Paterson
Raj Pathak
Stewart Patterson
Clare Pattinson
Kunaal Pattni
Mario Pavan
Gary Peacock
Nicholas Peacock
Jennifer Pearson
Laraine Pearson
Ian Peart
Trevor Peat
Kevin Pegg
Billy Peat
Ruth Pegler
John Pembroke
Jordan Pepperall
Kevin Percival
Jerome Pereira
Frederick Perry
Katie Perry
Baljinder Phagura
Linda Pham
Alex Phillips
David Phillips
James Phillips
John Phillips
Jack Pickering
David Pierce
Scott Pillinger
Michael Pinkerton
John Pinnock
Mario Pires
Gordon Pithouse
Victoria Pitman
Alexander Planitzer
Kevin Pomeroy
Octavian Popovich
Alec Porter
Clive Porter
Michael Porter
Shaun Potter
Hayley Poulter
Richard Poulter
Emily-Rose Powell
Geraint Powell
Margaret Powell
Martin Power
Andrew Powis
Abigail Poyntz-Wright
Natalija Poznanskiene
Colin Prime
John Prior
Andrew Pullen
Kevan Purcell

R

Cloe Raan
Holly Radcliffe
Mark Radford
Mehran Radnejad
Mohammed Rafiq
Renuka Ragupathy
Jagjit Rai
Melanie Ralph
Paul Randall
Stuart Andrew Rands
Becky Ray
John Reay
Lisa Redfern
James Reece
James Rees
Claire Reeves
John Regan
Gavin Reid
Aaron Renker
Suzanne Renton
James Reynolds
Mark Richards
Simon Richards
Wayne Richardson
Andrew Rickman
Denis Ring
Dimitrios Rizos
James Roantree
Simon Roberts
Simon Roberts
Matthew Roberts
Lily-May Roberts
Brian Robertson
Stephen Robertson
Paul Robilliard

SEVERN TUNNEL JUNCTION 2016 saw the replacement of the overbridge by the station to attain sufficient OLE clearance. In this view the new beam is being lifted into position over the up and down tunnel lines. The Severn Tunnel is behind the photographer in this view, looking towards Newport

ROLL OF HONOUR

Alan Roderick
Robert Rodriguez
Adam Rogers
Christopher Rolfe
Josh Rollins
Steven Rose
Julian Ross
Paul Roszkowski
John Rowe
James Rowland
Gareth Rowley
Leigh Rumble
Mark Rusdale
Laura Rusholme
Timothy Ryan
Craig Ryan

S
Irina Sabatina
Alfonso Saco Diaz
Paul Sadd
Nadia Salami
Alejandro Salazar-Rodriguez
Shyam Samani
Vinod Sampong
Alejandro Sanchez Tejeda
James Sanders
Philippa Sanders
Luisa Sanetti
Caroline Saunders
Ruma Saurabh
Darren Saving
David Scarrott
Helen Schofield
James Scholes
Daniel Schorah
Elizabeth Scott
Neil Scott
Ricky Scott
Samantha Scott
Adrian Scourfield
Anthony Scruton
Andrew Searle
Jonathan Seegolun
Erica Sells
Mark Senior
Adrian Sereda
Graham Serrell
Zaahra Shaamile
Ahmed Shahid
Peshang Shaho
Shalini Shalini
Vikas Shandal
Sourabh Sharma
Shifaly Sharma
Robert Sharp
Chris Shaw
Oliver Shaw
Sarah Shaw
Ben Shearing
Mark Shellard
Richard Shellard
Richard Sheppard
Zhan Shi
Gillian Shields
Ian Shirley
Gift Sibanda
Navjot Sidhu
Aleks Sienkiewicz
Joseph Simmons
Neil Simon
Robert Simpson
Andrew Sims
Christopher Sims
Guriqbal Singh
Jaspinder Singh
Derek Sledge
Victoria Smale
Charles Smalley
Clive Smith
Martin Smith
Michael Smith
Paul Smith
Robert Smith
Theo Smith
Aleksandra Sobieszek
Malgorzata Soltys
Karl Somers
Mark Somers
Jasvender Soumal
George Sowerby
Afroditi Spanou
Craig Speirs
Andrew Spencer
Benjamin Spencer
John Spencer

SEVERN TUNNEL JUNCTION In September 2017 the new structure and enhanced gauge clearance is ready for overhead wire installation. Behind the bridge on the left was the Amenity Block for the Severn Tunnel Junction traincrew depot, sadly closed in 1987. Staff at 'The Tunnel' were renowned for their helpfulness and once took a ballast train for the author all the way to Fishguard Harbour.

Roll of honour

Matthew Spencer
Andrew Sperring
David Spray
Balasubramaniam Sribalamayoran
Vythi Sritharan
Robert Stacey
John Stamp
David Standidge
James Stanford
Paul Stanford
Marta Stanulewicz
David Steele
Grahame Stephens
Kathryn Stephens
Robert Stephenson
Janet Stevens
John Stevens
Margaret Stevens
Karl Stevenson
Shaun Stewardson
Brendan Straffen
Grant Stratton
Graham Stubbings
Kirstie Stuka
Robert Sully
Byron Summers
Philip Summers
Kuldeep Sungher
Mark Swan
Peter Swann
Claire Sweeney
Thomas Sweeney
Dennis Sweet
Adam Szpytman

T

Graeme Tandy
Joyce Tang
Mathew Tanner
Andrew Tappern
Adolis Tarasevicius
Sean Tarpey
James Tarr
Arlene Tatton
Nigel Taylor
Robert Taylor
Stephen Taylor
William Taylor
Jonathan Tearle
Chuan Jiet Teo
James Terry
Marcus Tett
Thames Valley Signalling Centre and its predecessors
Hannah Theobald
Parmjot Thiarha
Geoffrey Thomas
Huw Thomas
Robert Thomas
Samantha Thomas
Elle-Mae Thompson
James Thompson
Mike Thompson
Neil Thompson
Christopher Thurbon
Nico Tillema
Matt Tindall
Donna Tingey
Daniel Tipper
Rebecca Tipper
Leslie Tipping
Dango Toby
Paul Topping
Laura Townsend
Nick Travis
Katherine Trevorrow
Kirsty Tunstall
Paul Turfrey
John Turnbull
Andy Turner
Jonathan Turton
Lee Tyack
Mariusz Tyszka

U

Princess Udenkolo
Godswill Udo
Paul Urban

V

Khushil Vadher
Benedict Vallely
Hector Varela
Anuj Vats
Neil Vowell
Anusha Vuppulri

CARDIFF EAST (NEWTOWN)
A track relaying job concludes as a prelude to electrification works in 2018.

Roll of Honour

W

Marcus Wadhams
Amy Wagstaff
Farah Wahab
Sultana Wahab
Hannah Wakefield
Eve Walkden
Callum Walker
Charles Walker
Max Walker
Aisling Wall
Alexander Walls
John Walsh
Tom Walsh
Jake Walton
John Walton
Lawrence Walton
Ben Ward
Ian Ward
Stephen Ward
Matthew Warren
Laura Warwick
Richard Waters
Robert Watkins
Carla Watts
Edward Watts
Mark Wearing
David Webb
Gary Webb
Steve Webb
Stephen Weitz
Andrew Welch
Christopher Wells
Mary Wells
Dawn Welsh
Daniel West
Daniel West
David West
Anton Westwood
Nicola Whaley
Colin Wheelans
Benjamin Wheeldon
Peter Whiley
Richard Whinnett
Ann White
Bryan White
David White
Martin White
Amy Whitty
Emma Wicks
Peter Wiles
Bob Wilkes
Bronwen Wilkes
Noemi Willenbockel
Chloe Williams
David Williams
Kelly Williams
Mark Williams
Ryan Williams
William Williams
Helen Wills
Paul Wills
Andrew Willson
Ken Willy
Abbie Wilson
Christopher Wilson
Daniel Wilson
Dean Wilson
John Wilson
Peter Wilson
Ron Wilson
Lee Wiltshire
Adela Winfield
Mark Winwood
Stuart Witts
Charles Wood
Christopher Wood
Colin Wood
Michael Woodburn
Amelia Woodley
Glyn Woods
Thomas Woodworth
Robert Wormald
Joel Worthington
Brian Wortman
Karen Wright
Jonathan Wright
Mark Wright
Gerald Wrigley

CARDIFF EAST This night-time track laying and lowering ready for electrification works took place in 2018, and continues as this book goes to press.

Roll of honour

X

Paulson Xavier

Y

Gareth Yanulevitch
Gareth Yates
David Youell
Rosalind Young
Mahad Yusuf
Mohsin Yusuf

Z

Mourad Zadia

Amey

Nicola Hindle
Kelvin Holder
Paul Lazarus
Simon Rhoden
Annabel Springthorpe
Richard Walker
Anne Watters
HOPS Train Team

Balfour Beatty

Matthew Brassington
Mark Bullock
Mick Rayner
Pete Webb
Nicholas Watson

Bechtel

Tarek Chamseddine
Paul Coates
Darren Coleman
Tony Gordon
Bill Henry
Mike Jackson
Dave Lawson
Scott Lerski
Vin Maini
Amar Mohammad
Rich Moore
Stephen Moore
Brian Nichols
Doug Parker
Nigel Pennington
Steve Plyler
John Rife
Ken Willy

READING Sparks fly as the rail is broken ready to start a relay job to address the next phase of the Reading remodelling, executed in the period 2010 to 2015.